An Insider's Guide to the Injured Brain

An Insider's Guide to the Injured Brain:

A workbook for survivors and those who support them

by

Ruth Curran, MS

Mary Lanzavecchia

Sara Mark, Editor

Caitlin Lanzavecchia, Production Coordinator

An Insider's Guide to the Injured Brain

Rolling Mulligan Inc.
3410 Hawk St.
San Diego, CA 92103

To all of those looking for the laughter and joy we found, writing this book.

Mary & Ruth

TABLE OF CONTENT

EXERCISE LIST

You will find copies of all workbook pages on a secret page on www.insidersguidetotheinjuredbrain.com. Click on the button that says EXERCISES on the Home page. The secret password, the one you get by reading this, is *openplease*.

CHAPTER ONE
Introduction

Meet Ruth

*The seeds of **The Insider's Guide to the Injured Brain** were planted by an unexpected result.*

*A few years ago I wrote and published a book about building a better brain, **Being Brain Healthy: What my brain injury taught me and how it can change your life**. Triggered by the car accident that left me in the deep fog of a brain injury, the book focused on how I navigated my 18-month active healing process and how I used that process to think, do, and be better, all by living life more fully.*

*My goal for **Being Brain Healthy** was to help those looking to improve brain function find ways to thrive by turning up the volume and adding color to what they were already doing every single day. I set out to provide practical, everyday inspiration and exercises to turn daily tasks into brain boosters.*

Very quickly I realized that the message went well beyond my original intention.

The first clues came from fellow writers who were helping me promote. They told me of their loved ones who were navigating strokes, coping with traumatic brain injuries, recovering from brain tumors, and dealing with the confusion brought on by chemotherapy. Each person I talked to could relate on a deeper level than any of us had imagined.

Then the bigger "Ah Ha" moments started popping up – ones that took me completely by surprise. A woman shared the story of how her husband, a survivor of multiple strokes, was wrongly diagnosed with depression because he couldn't find the right words to define his experience. A man reached out to tell me that no one had explained that his wife could lose and rebuild depth perception and that my saying so had helped them turn a corner on the road to recovery. Another man told me that his wife no longer wanted to leave the house after she had suffered a brain injury from falling off her bike. He thought she had just given up until he read about sensory overload and realized that there were things he could do and talk to her about that actually helped her.

Huh….

*I remember the moment when I **got it** that so many people from so many walks of life and in so many situations know someone who is either in the fog or emerging from the fog left by a brain injury. Chances are none of them have any idea how it feels to be inside that injured brain. For me, that was a huge and unexpected shift in perspective.*

I started to see not just from inside my imperfect brain but from inside the perspective of those who deal with people like me, muddling through post brain injury, and I realized 1) how incredibly frustrating all of this is for those living with us and 2) just how little they all actually know.

What a strange feeling to understand that not only did my

book, the one I had poured my heart and soul into, have a different impact than I had intended, but also that my work was nowhere near done.

I had not set out to give a look inside what can happen in a changed brain and what that feels like and means for day-to-day life. That whole idea was so far beyond the scope of what I thought I was doing! That, however, was exactly what more people than I could have imagined, took away after reading my book….

*Here are some of the facts of life that I shared in **Being Brain Healthy** that readers told me bridged the divide for them:*

- *At some point during recovery, many with brain injuries are labeled as depressed. Much of the time, that lack of motivation or unwillingness to talk is not depression at all. In actuality, it is more likely to be apathy, lack of initiation, not knowing how to find the right explanation for their experience, or just plain physical and mental exhaustion.*
- *Sensory overload is common after a brain injury. Sensitivity to light, sound, smells, touch, tastes, and combinations of sensory activities even in small doses can set a recovering brain over the edge, resulting in a shutdown.*
- *Plain and simple, changes in behavior and emotional control are **normal** post brain injury. **This is the rule, not the exception**.*
- *Humor, empathy, and appreciating beauty are complicated processes that just might take time, patience, and persistence to rebuild. And yes, in many cases they need to be rebuilt or at least rekindled.*

The challenge and the scope of this work shifted and, in some respects, got so much bigger than me. How could I effectively explain, from the inside, something that no one else can see or hold in their hands? How could I possibly describe something when, in

3

the most frustrating moments, words are not readily available and expressing multidimensional ideas is just not happening?

I imagine that it is incredibly frustrating for those on the outside who are trying to figure out what is going on inside the brain of someone they care about post brain injury. That person looks the same as yesterday—no scars, no casts, no bruises—but is acting, reacting, and interacting differently.

*What hit me was this: these are all issues that can be **eased by simply raising the level of understanding** – knowing, making small shifts to, and adjusting the environment can change the quality of life for both partners navigating the healing process.*

Just knowing, seeing, recognizing…that is big.

I also knew that I could not do this alone.

Meet Mary

When Ruth asked me to join her on this project, she prefaced her request with a warning—writing this book could be difficult for me since I was less than a year out from my brain injury. She cautioned me again, warning me that the process of writing this book and revisiting the memories would likely stir difficult waters. She told me to think it over before giving her my answer.

Mentally, I had answered long before the words came out of my mouth. Still, I told her I would think it over, and so I did.

In hindsight, though, I didn't think about what she was trying to say, about the triggers and the emotions that would come. I thought about the writing process and how the writer in me wanted—no, needed—something to hold my feet to the fire of accountability. In the months following the accident, I tried to push myself to write on a regular basis, but my inability to hold my focus chipped away at my confidence. That, above anything else, was my fear in agreeing to co-author this book. I feared being seen as incompetent, and the writing process is very revealing.

Looking back now, there were so many areas I had shored up my personal edges for fear of being seen as damaged goods. I knew my cognitive processing had changed after my accident, but I refused to acknowledge, let alone accept, those changes. I feared acceptance meant permanence and permanence meant who I was was lost forever. That fear dictated my actions to deflect attention and actively conceal what was and wasn't going on inside my injured brain. Perhaps above all, that fear inhibited my healing.

*I jumped into this project with little hesitation and even less awareness of both the pain and healing that would come of it. I truly thought I had little to explore personally because my brain injury **wasn't that bad**. Additionally, I was raised with the belief that you could just "think yourself well." Fools, as they say, rush in.*

Armed with those two misconceptions, Ruth and I began writing during early morning video calls. Carefully, I tried to maintain distance between our words and my emotion, denying the full applicability to my situation. Some days were easier than others. I don't remember the first, or the second, or even the 500th time the reality of what we were discussing or writing set off a string of light bulb moments in my head and my heart.

At some point, I realized the more I worked to drop the façade and open myself, the greater the personal connection became. And when I shared that awareness with my family, real healing began for all of us. Those moments of vulnerability and awareness brought a different, more authentic voice to my writing and my life.

During our writing and editing process, Ruth and I coined many expressions that were fitting for life and quite often, specifically life after a brain injury. One of my favorites that is written out on a Post-It Note stuck to my computer screen, has become both my healing and life philosophy: Back up, accept, and move to next.

A few weeks ago, I passed the 2-year mark since my accident. In the days before that, Ruth and I reread our original introduction. We both laughed at our original efforts. The words "brain injury" were carefully avoided, delicately opting for brain changes or brain challenges. I know I didn't want to claim my own brain injury at the time—I wasn't ready to back up and accept—so, I carefully avoided the label as part of my denial process. Over the course of the last 2 years, but more specifically the last 16 months we've spent writing, I've reflected a great deal and now I am ready to move to next.

Our Shared Mission

Together we set out to shed some light on how it feels from the inside of a brain injury, to create a bit of understanding, and to open the door for healing conversations.

We wanted to focus on building bridges to healing and on creating a way for survivors and their support systems to become true partners in healing—forging a shared pathway that might lead to deeper understanding and a commitment to living a richer, fuller, and more fulfilling life during the process. We invite you to embrace this process together and work through the layers of misunderstanding.

We knew that our personal experiences were far from unique and far from inclusive, so we set out to talk to other survivors and their support to better understand and honor their journeys. We interviewed many people as part of this process and, peppered throughout the rest of this book, you will find their thoughts, stories, impressions, reactions, and learnings set apart in italics.

Every conversation, story, and piece of wisdom that came

as part of this process lead us closer and closer to something even bigger. Here, in a nutshell is what we learned:

> *The fog associated with an injured brain is individual but, just as fog does in nature, it can consume all who are near.*

This book, we realized, needed to do more than just include or give lip-service to support; it needed to speak directly to those who find themselves unexpectedly lost in the same fog as their loved one—a fog that is often every bit as difficult for support to understand and navigate from the outside as it is for the survivor to translate from the inside.

"But, you look so normal" was a common refrain amongst those who shared their stories. It hit us that the battle was to get past *looking normal* in order to navigate hidden challenges and struggles waging in the background.

Often, well intentioned loved ones seek medical clarification and recovery time frames to aid their understanding.

However, as they and countless others can attest, there is no diagnostic tool, magic bullet, or standard timeframe for recovery. Instead, the recovery process can be better understood through the common experiences, changes, and behaviors that tend to occur within the lives of people who are working through the fog of a brain injury (even when they look "Oh, so normal").

This revelation brought a renewed awareness that there is, in fact, a unifying, but little discussed, frustration among all who live with and are affected by a brain that has been changed, regardless of the origins of that change. Both support *and* survivors often spend a great deal of emotional and physical energy trying to make things *normal again*, meaning exactly as they once were, neglecting the opportunity to define and find a new normal. Though it is easy to get discouraged, it is important to remember that these are all issues that we can manage by having *this* conversation and raising the level of understanding.

We have not set out to reinvent the wheel by repackaging clinical information already available. Instead, this book is intended to:

- Give a look at what it feels like inside the fog of an injured brain.
- Provide valuable resources, insights, and workbook activities.
- And, help pave the way for all those affected by that ominous fog to become partners in the healing process.

> *Did you know, you are more likely to know someone who has a brain injury than you are to know someone who has cancer?*

Think about that one for a moment. No joke: 1.8 million people are diagnosed with a brain injury in the emergency room *every year.* Another 600,000 have strokes that significantly change their thinking.

> *Almost 3 million people are directly impacted by brain injuries every single year.*

We know that those statistics are not wholly inclusive.

Neither of us was diagnosed with a brain injury in the ER because we looked and gave the impression that we felt *normal*.

These numbers don't include those working through cloudy thinking from conditions no one keeps statistics on such as "chemo-brain", after-effects of anesthesia, neurodegenerative diseases like MS and Parkinson's, or other age-related conditions that can simply change how a person thinks.

The next issue is tougher to address because it is far less tangible and incredibly difficult to quantify. There is no specific *look* to someone caught in the fog of a brain injury. The vast majority look like they did before injury with few, if any, noticeable changes to their physical appearance. There are no scars, bruises, or casts that might indicate a change. There are rarely obvious symptoms of a chronic brain injury. There is no special parking area for people who regularly forget where they parked, let alone why they came to that store. In fact, more often than not, from the outside, nothing out of the ordinary seems to be happening, and still the struggle wages within.

That last sentence may summarize the single greatest frustration for all involved. From the inside, how can you explain something that no one else can see or feel, especially when the right words are not readily available? Multiply that feeling by 100 and you, the reader, might capture the feelings of frustration, anxiety, and, sometimes, hopelessness, felt by those trapped inside the fog and confusion created by an injured or changed brain.

Those feelings are mirrored by caregivers, friends, family, co-workers, and others – collectively, we call them the support. From the outside, they see a person who looks the same as they did yesterday but is acting differently and they don't fully understand why.

Our first step is to look at brain injuries, traumatic and otherwise, as a whole: where they start, how they build, what to look for, what we can and can't see or measure, and how to understand it all.

CHAPTER TWO
What is a brain injury?

In this section you will find the basics about brain injury. Our intent is not to be factually exhaustive nor to include every possible origin of brain injury. Instead, we hope to build a foundation of understanding in the form of a conversation. We know that even the driest facts may be useful, helpful, or eye-opening for someone and might open the door to healing.

Take what you need from the following section and use it however it fits best in your life.

> *A brain injury is the uninvited guest to the party.*

According to the Center for Disease Control:

Traumatic brain injury (TBI) is an insult to the brain caused by an external physical force, such as occurs in a motor vehicle accident, falls, assaults, sports-related injury, and proximity to explosions/blast injuries. A concussion is a mild TBI.

11

Let's expand that definition slightly to include some diseases that are degenerative and may, in some cases, be hereditary (MS, Parkinson's disease, Alzheimer's disease, to name a few) and are not typically associated with *brain injury*. Additionally, chemically induced assaults on the brain (chemotherapy, anesthesia, other medications) are more common than you think and can result in brain injury.

Regardless of origin though, brain injuries carry similar hidden symptoms and issues that hinder thinking, processing, and living. So, for our purposes, we will consider them all brain injuries, and all the exercises and insights found in this book apply equally.

Classes of Brain Injury

In this section, we focus on three types of assault on the brain: impact injuries, chemically induced injuries, and disease related injuries.

Impact Injuries

More often than not, when people think about a brain injury, they think of one caused by an impact. A hard hit during a contact sport, a car accident, or a fall are commonly thought of causes for impact injuries. Here is a bit more about the dynamics of brain injuries caused by impact.

Your brain, surrounded by cerebrospinal fluid, floats inside your skull. When the impact is minor, the fluid acts as a shock absorber, protecting your brain. When the impact is more severe, however, the brain bangs around inside the skull much like a ball inside a racquetball court, crashing from one side to the other.

Let's take a look at some particulars to better understand what that means.

The first type of impact brain injury is a coup / countrecoup injury. In this case, there is a direct blow to the body that is severe enough to whip the head back and forth. The force overpowers the shock absorbing fluid, resulting in the brain striking the inner skull (the coup). As the head slows down and stops its motion, the brain then hits the opposite side of the skull (the countrecoup).

The second type of impact injury, one commonly associated with sports, is a rotational injury. The head rapidly rotates from one side to another, causing shearing and straining of brain tissues.

Another type of impact injury is a blast injury. This type of injury creates a unique and complex situation because it adds another element: the pressure from the blast itself. Those who suffer a blast injury deal not just with the physical impacts, as found in both coup / countrecoup and rotational injuries, they also face changes in the brain that come as a result of rapid and dramatic pressure changes in the environment.

In all cases, delicate neural pathways in the brain can become damaged, causing a variety of issues.

Many of these injuries are simply labeled *concussions*. Using this common label often reduces the significance of the injury and minimizes its impact on daily life. Traditionally, a concussion is treated like a minor bump that will, given a day or so, heal. This dangerous point of view only serves to create frustration for those dealing with the very real issues that accompany a concussion.

A concussion *is* a traumatic brain injury. That is worth repeating and repeating until it sinks in:

A concussion is a traumatic brain injury.

Concussions frequently come with changes in thinking and functioning. It does not matter if those changes last a minute, a year, or a lifetime.

Recently, the medical community has expanded its focus

13

and renamed the after-effects of a concussion *Post-Concussive Syndrome*. This recognizes that there are ramifications and continued challenges after an injury. Identifying that post-concussive syndrome is real can create a more supportive and empathetic environment – one that focuses on healing and rebuilding instead of waiting for the symptoms to pass.

Chemically Induced Injuries

All kinds of chemicals, environmental and prescribed, create changes in and shift the balance of the brain's chemical and electrical activity. That shift alters how the brain functions.

- Postoperative delirium is a real condition linked to anesthesia, especially in older adults, and causes confusion and memory loss that sometimes lingers.
- Cancer patients being treated with chemotherapy can experience memory loss, issues with problem solving, and can struggle to find the right words.
- Any medication that is intended to regulate emotion or self-control alters neurochemistry, and that chemical shift changes how we think and react to the world.

Sometimes a cure or treatment for a disease can be harmful to your brain. The tradeoffs are insanely hard to measure but very real. Because of this, it is necessary that informed conversations about the side-effects of prescription medications, anesthesia, and chemotherapy become more mainstream.

Medical practitioners often fail to mention the potential brain changes associated with cures or treatments for illness because they believe those conversations might be counter-productive to patient care.

In order to be an effective partner in healing, it is critical for those who live with or care for people exposed to these types of treatments be aware of the potential changes in thinking, emotional control, and ability to function.

Opening the conversation about these types of brain changes might just change how we treat each other.

Disease Related Injuries

This class of brain injury is trickier to think about because the brain injury, itself, is often masked and consumed by the physical aspects of the disease.

This is a very broad area but considering a few specific examples of changes in the brain helps shed some light.

- In **Multiple Sclerosis (MS)**, the damaged myelin coating around the nerve fibers of the central nervous system (CNS) interferes with the transmission of signals between the brain and the rest of the body. The structural changes within the nerve fibers can create dramatic shifts in how the brain works.

- A **stroke** is a sudden interruption in blood flow to the brain that cuts off oxygen and nutrients, causing brain cells to die, blocking neural pathways. Those blocked pathways cut off communication and nourishment to all parts of the brain down that line.

- **Alzheimer's Disease (AD)** is a condition where masses (plaques and tangles) form and grow in the brain with no known outside trigger. By blocking neural pathways, the masses prevent normal chemical and electrical firing, thereby prohibiting healthy functioning.

- Some forms of **Lupus** change the structure of the blood vessels in the brain, thereby altering pressure and shifting the ability to process information.

These types of changes in the brain can act in the same way as a blocked or injured pathway from an impact or chemically induced injury. From inside the brain, the source of the damage makes no difference. An assault on the brain is an assault on the brain, and the origin becomes irrelevant. The connections are lost and without attention will no longer work.

Historically, degenerative and progressive diseases have not been considered brain injuries. Separating this type of condition is easier from a clinician's standpoint, but from a caregiver's perspective, it is critical to see the whole picture and understand how all kinds of changes in the brain create daily challenges.

These disease-related changes go undocumented for three primary reasons:

- Medical practitioners want to be able to fix the problem, and right now there is no pill or protocol to fix a brain injury.
- Science is evolving, and there is still so much we don't understand about the connection between brain and disease.
- It is difficult for patients to acknowledge and adjust to what feels like yet another hurdle.

Final Thoughts

Brain injuries happen throughout the entire lifespan and happen as part of our everyday lives. It is really important to remember that there is no minimum or maximum age for a brain injury. It is the toddler who falls and bumps their head. It is the child who tumbles off the jungle gym. It is the teen who hits a tree while skiing. It is the mom with full arms who slips on black ice. It is the grandfather who loses his balance when picking up the newspaper. It is any of us. It is all of us. It happens every day.

And, again, the brain doesn't care about the source of injury; a brain injury is a brain injury is a brain injury.

The after effects of an injury are very real, very common, and can be very confusing for everyone involved. While we openly admit there is still so much more to explore, learn, and understand, we do know that every single tip, trick, and exercise provided here will help you start the rebuilding process.

We hope this book will serve as a roadmap and help you better understand the process of healing. Through that, you may find comfort, ease, and empowerment. And above all, we hope you begin to build bridges to better functioning while creating partnerships in healing.

CHAPTER THREE
Defining Normal

When you are trying so desperately to hang on to who you were, you paralyze yourself. - Mary

What now?

Now, as a team, you learn to build a bridge to a new normal.

According to Merriam-Webster, the simple definition of normal is: *Usual or ordinary: not strange.*

When we think about normal we think about being able to do those everyday things that get us from morning to night without too many glitches.

- Normal is successfully following the simple steps to brushing your teeth.
- Normal is being able to plan and pay your bills.
- Normal is knowing what to do when the phone or the doorbell rings.

19

- Normal is getting to the grocery store and bank without getting lost.
- Normal is being able to find an outfit that does not feel too restrictive, too tight, too scratchy, too heavy, too clingy.
- Normal is being able to look at a do-list and not get overwhelmed and retreat.
- Normal is being able to read the words on a page without having them turn to dots.
- Normal is being able to walk outside and have your eyes adjust to the light.
- Normal is knowing that the right word will come out of your mouth.
- Normal is being in a familiar place and knowing how you will react.

Normal captures how we interact with the world every day. A brain injury changes that normal.

My normal was my mom recognizing my children, but that changed. -LW

My normal was being able to go into a restaurant and sit at any table without panicking, but that changed. -AF

My normal was my dad being patient, but that changed. -IM

My normal was planning and planting a garden every year, but that changed. -DR

My normal was writing in my journal regularly, but that changed. -JE

My normal was watching a movie and understanding the dialogue without subtitles, but that changed. -JM

My normal was my wife organizing our lives, but that changed. -DC

My normal was my son being playful, but that changed. -RN

My normal was being able to understand what my professor was talking about, but that changed. -CA

CHAPTER FOUR
Redefine Normal

Brain injury can change how you react, interact, and function in the world. Once you start to recognize those changes and you stop fighting them so ferociously, that is where rebuilding begins.

We are conditioned to think that normal – that state where everything feels familiar and predictable– doesn't change, or at least not suddenly. It might feel a bit unsettling to think about living in a world where *normal* is a moving target.

But, we do.

In order to thrive in fluid conditions, we must find a way to stop struggling.

Think about this: Your normal is a function of what your life looks like today. That normal takes into account your health, mood, stage of life, job, relationship status, family, political climate, and so much more. Your normal is dependent upon factors subject to continual change. It makes sense that normal is both situational and time dependent.

That is a pretty big shift in thinking for most people. We tend to think that the big changes in life, like those that come with aging, are gradual and time allows for adaptation. The learning curve is not that steep because we have time to adjust.

There are two perspectives to consider when starting to redefine normal and both center on fears.

First, for the person inside the fog of a brain injury:

- It is getting past the fear that you are not going to be the person you once were.
- It is getting past the fear that you won't measure up.
- It is getting past the fear that you won't like the person you have become.
- It is getting past the fear that others won't accept the person you are right now.
- It is getting past the fear that you will not be able to do your work.

Second, for the support system:

- It is getting past the fear that you have forever lost the person you loved.
- It is getting past the fear that you can't handle this alternate future.
- It is getting past the fear that you are not enough.

The fog that comes with a brain injury does not just stay inside the head of the person with the injury—it creeps out and consumes the support system and touches all aspects of life.

When life changes in a flash, like with a brain injury or traumatic event, suddenly everything feels out of place. It is difficult to understand exactly what is happening and why, no less try to tease out some sanity.

In redefining normal, all parties involved must:

- Take a step back and drop the resistance to change – accept that life is not what it was yesterday.
- Actively look for changes in functioning—emotional control, problem solving, ability to complete tasks, producing the right words, level of engagement in life—*all of it.*
- Recognize and accept the changes as they are and figure out how to move forward.
- Acknowledge that normal will change and that there is no finish line that will take you back to where you were before this journey began.

When we, together, stop fighting and find the calm in the stream, life feels more manageable, less out of control, and easier to face.

But You Look So Normal

With millions of people walking through the challenges that come with a brain injury, chances are you are interacting with a survivor who might look normal to you.

Seeing beyond the façade is challenging and takes patience and persistence. Anticipating an invisible problem requires a deeper level of understanding.

Signs of processing challenges show up as changes – changes that are open for interpretation and changes that could be interpreted as mood or approach or attitude. Changes in level of engagement in life, reactions, speech, willingness to communicate, emotional control, and relationships all might be signaling changes in brain function post injury.

What we are focusing on here are those hidden changes that survivors—those who have lived inside an injured brain—experience on a whole different level and many times, are unable to express.

The challenge for everyone—survivors and their support—is understanding that there are processes going on that not everyone can see, feel, or even grasp.

We know, first hand, that:

Sometimes my quick temper was not anger at all. It was overwhelm. -Mary

My unwillingness to participate in life was not depression. It was simply not having the energy to care. -Ruth

Running into the same couch was not from a lack of focus. It was my loss of depth perception. -Ruth

Listening to audiobooks was not me being lazy. It was a strategy to keep my love of books, even when my eyes were unable to focus. -Mary

When I set the pan on fire, I was not being careless. It was my inability to follow the steps in the right order. -Ruth

When I missed appointments, it was not that I believed they were unimportant. It was simply that I lost control of the organization and order that kept my life on track. -Mary

Staying quiet was not me withdrawing. It was not being able to find the right words to express what was really going on. -Mary

Not participating in a conversation did not mean I was

uninterested or did not care. I was unable to track and keep up. -Ruth

Not laughing at a joke did not mean that it wasn't funny. I was not able to understand the complexities and subtleties of humor. -Ruth

*Cleaning the room, obsessively, did not signal a problem. It was my means to regain order—some semblance of control and eliminate distractions—to regain and retain focus.
  -Mary*

It is easy to make assumptions about what seemingly benign behaviors—a kicked couch or missed appointment—mean. We try to fit them into what we believe is a *normal* part of daily life. When those behaviors don't make sense or happen repeatedly, take a step back. Put the behaviors in context. Try to see past what *was* normal and redefine what *is* normal.

Back up, accept, move to next.

CHAPTER FIVE
Building Bridges: The Four Corners

In the remainder of this book we are attempting to separate functions so that you can better understand how each works in order to begin the rebuilding process. Keep in mind, however, that we can never truly separate brain functions. Everything works together, in concert, and overlaps. Attention is a part of cognitive functioning; cognitive functioning mingles with emotional control; vision changes impact everything—our attention, cognitive abilities, and emotions.

With that in mind, each section will have a bridge to the next. We will build the bridge from attention to cognitive functioning, then a bridge from cognitive functioning to emotional control, and finally a bridge from all three to changes in vision. Each of those bridges will deal with the overlap—that inseparable space between—and will include journal pages to gather and record your thoughts, and consider how *you* build that bridge.

Weaving the Fabric of a Brain Injury

It might help to think about brain injury as a fabric, woven with multicolored threads from all involved in the process—some threads from the survivor and some threads from the support—the caregivers, service providers, co-workers, family, friends, teachers. Those individual threads represent changes in attention, emotional control, thinking, vision, and so much more that weave together to create an unfamiliar fabric that blankets life post brain injury.

When any one or more of these threads get pulled, everything changes:

- Attention waivers and senses overload.
- Thinking goes off track.
- Emotional control slips.
- Vision blurs.
- Systems shut down...

...and life spins in a different, sometimes unpredictable, direction.

CHAPTER SIX
Why a Workbook

It felt like life was just happening to me. I was not an active participant—I was just sitting there in the stream, bobbing up and down. If I could slow those pieces down enough to separate them, I knew I had a shot at some sort of control; if I could just slow down enough to breathe. –Ruth

When we began writing this book, we hadn't envisioned a workbook—a toolbox, yes, but not a workbook. It was not until we were well into the writing and development process that we realized that this project was about building, re-building, and understanding the pieces that held life together.

The turning point came after we created *and* completed an exercise intended to give us perspective before we continued writing. We used this exercise (now Exercise I in this book) to notice and note everything that we do every single day. That opened our eyes to the real value of what we set out to do.

Our initial intention was to give a peek into what it feels like inside a brain post brain injury. Exercise 1 helped us realize that successful rebuilding after a brain injury *was* and *is* about slowing life down enough to notice what is happening around us—really looking at the pieces and understanding not just how things work but how they work together.

With the idea of breaking down moments into their components—creating those snapshots –we could hold them at arm's length and look at the scene from a variety of perspectives. Each component helps build a foundation—a viewing platform to stand on and a place to start building

When we started to create exercises, something big happened. The process revealed the interconnection and importance of each component involved in painting a whole picture. We found that even though some of the exercises may seem obvious and elementary, it is important to do all of them, in order. Placing each block, in sequence, as we build that foundation is so important to this process, to make sense of how it all fits together.

The exercises in this book are not just healing for survivors, they are also incredibly healing for support. Each of the exercises opens a dialogue and an avenue for all to become partners—active participants—in the healing process.

Therein lies the hope.

You will find copies of all workbook pages on a secret page on www.insidersguidetotheinjuredbrain.com. Click on the button that says EXERCISES on the Home page. The secret password, the one you get by reading this, is *openplease*.

CHAPTER SEVEN
Our First Challenge: Keep a Week Long Log

*As part of writing this book, Ruth and I challenged ourselves to set aside a week to **pay attention** to all of the things we do each day. Our goal was to specifically focus on and record those tasks that require attention to detail and order.*

We knew that if we wanted to fully understand the role of attention and order in our daily lives we needed to dig deeper into how we manage our moments and what adjustments we make to what we have always done.

This whole exercise was like a mini-awakening for me. I kept a log as I moved through the week, noting the activities as directed and, after the first day or so, began noticing a couple of patterns.

*First, I realized just how many activities I do, **routinely**, that not only require a little of my attention but the **entirety** of my attention. Sustained attention is sometimes a challenge in my current functional life. That was a big wakeup call.*

Second, I was surprised by how many of the activities I recorded required active listening. In my new normal, real active listening is not just auditory. I need visual cues.

33

I hadn't fully realized the extent to which my hearing had changed since my accident, frequently leaving me struggling to decipher even the simplest of sentences. Here, from the last night of that exercise, is a glaring example of what I mean.

The night before the week-long challenge came to an end, I was up later than usual troubleshooting my internet connection. Before I crawled into bed, I shot off an email to Ruth explaining our scheduled Skype date may end up being a "regular phone" chat since our internet was down, but I'd let her know in the morning. A few hours into my sleep, I awoke with a panicked feeling. As I lay in the dark, I sifted through my emotions until I realized that I needed Skype and depended on the visual input it offered, affording me another sense to rely on while processing what I hear.   - Mary

Exercise 1: Week Long Log

This exercise is for both **S1 (Survivor) and S2 (Support).** The directions for both are the same for both **S1 and S2.**

The **goal** of this exercise is to help you notice the importance of attention and order in our lives. Nothing more—just notice and make note.

Start today and on these workbook pages, make a list of all the tasks where you must consciously pay attention. For example, brushing your teeth, making a pot of coffee, paying a bill, starting the car, getting the groceries to cook a meal, etc. Here, you are just noting the name of the task, not writing out the steps involved. Just name the activity.

Compare notes with each other.

Monday's Activities

Tuesday's Activities

Wednesday's Activities

Thursday's Activities

Friday's Activities

Saturday's Activities

Sunday's Activities

CHAPTER EIGHT

The First Corner: Changes in Attention

Attention is a super function. Without it, nothing really makes sense. In the context of everyday life, attention is the process that, at any given moment, enhances some information and inhibits other information. With that in mind, it is no surprise that attention is one of the hardest brain functions to describe.

The key questions, simple as they may sound, are these:

- How do we, moment to moment, pay attention to the information that is most important?

- How do we keep from being overloaded?

- What happens to the information we selectively choose to ignore?

- Is attention something that we can summon by sheer will?

What we let in—that sensory information that gets our attention—shapes our moments, colors our worlds, and defines what makes up our very existence.

Think about that – *it's big*. Our experience and how we understand the world is spun by our senses. By some process, one that we may never fully understand, we weave those threads into the fabric of our experience. How can we describe this creative process that brings the whole world together and, in essence, *creates* our reality?

Clues to just how complicated and all-encompassing sifting and sorting through information really is can be found in the brain's anatomy.

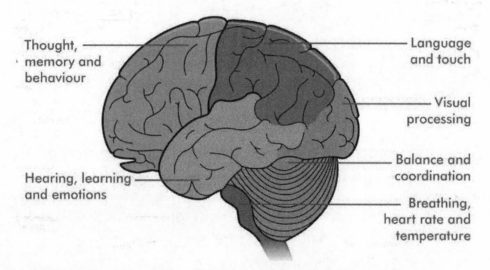

Thought, memory and behaviour

Hearing, learning and emotions

Language and touch

Visual processing

Balance and coordination

Breathing, heart rate and temperature

Even though those sections and functions in the brain appear to be independent, they are truly *inter*dependent. Paying attention to life's details requires all the parts of the brain to work together, at one time.

Attentional Blinks

Though people conceptualize attention in a variety of ways, when working from inside the injured brain, it is particularly important to understand the attentional blink, an event known to rip the fabric of the moment.

Attentional blinks are those moments that pop up out of nowhere and steal your focus. They can be important, irrelevant, or just add color to an unfolding scene. From inside a brain injury, stopping to evaluate an attentional blink can derail a thought process.

Here's an example of how this might work: You are sitting in Starbucks with a friend while she's telling you a story. The door opens. Out of the corner of your eye, you see a flash as the sun catches the metal door frame. You turn, spot the person walking in, and, suddenly, you have lost your place in the conversation. Your attention is now focused on that person as they move into line. That attentional blink derailed you and your place in the conversation.

Attentional blinks can also serve you. For example, you are talking on the phone. The dryer buzzes, signaling the shirt you want to wear is now ready. That is important information. Or, if you're hungry, you may notice a basket of delicious looking fruit on a nearby table. However, if you've just eaten, your attention may glide over that basket of fruit with barely a glance, dismissing it as irrelevant.

The critical point is to pick out the information that is most important and learn to dismiss those attentional blinks that are simply noise in the background.

Exercise 2 Part I: Attentional Blinks

> This exercise is for **S1 (Survivor) and S2 (Support).**
> The directions are the same for both **S1 and S2.**

Go to a public place—a coffee shop, a table at a grocery story, a bench in a park—with a magazine that interests you. In addition, bring this workbook and pen/pencil. Open your book to this page and put it under your magazine. Begin reading your magazine. *Every time* something pulls your attention away from your magazine, write it down in your workbook. Did you notice the bird flying by? Write it down. Did you notice a horn honking? Write it down. Did you notice that person yelling, the child's laugh, the dog's bark? Write it down. When you run out of space on this page go to the next page. Do this for 30 minutes. At the end of the day, evaluate if the attentional blinks you noted were important, (IMP), irrelevant (IRR), or just add color (COL). Next to each item, write: IMP, IRR, or COL.

Compare notes with each other.

CHANGES IN ATTENTION

Continue recording your observations here.

Wrap-Up

This exercise helps you identify just how often your attention is pulled away from the task at hand. Brain injury changes your ability to come back to where you left off and complete that task.

Noting and noticing how often this happens might help you gain an awareness of what is currently happening, while providing evidence of a more significant pattern. As you repeat this exercise in different settings you might even find ways to instantaneously adapt as you feel attentional blinks happening.

The critical pieces are to:

- Slow it all down,
- Figure out what is important in the scene, and
- See if a strategy to redirect focus appears.

Attention and Safety

After a brain injury, how we pay attention changes. Ironically, and perhaps cruelly, these changes are most difficult to see from inside the imperfect brain. The critical point, which is so obvious that it is often overlooked, is this: to recognize and understand the changes in our ability to pay attention, **we need to be able to pay attention**. It's much like a traffic circle, but there's no exit point.

Problems with attention are not just frustrating, annoying, and terribly inconvenient, they can also be dangerous.

Here is a pretty eye-opening statistic directly related to breaks in attention: 70% of all brain injury survivors will have at least one, but probably more, additional head injuries in their lifetime. As a result of the remnants of a previous brain injury, many survivors have had at least one lapse in attention that caused them to hit their head hard enough to change their brains, at least temporarily.

Yes, this is a sobering fact for those who have been there and back and, once again, find themselves walking through the fog of clouded thinking, looking for the way out.

About eight months after the car accident that started my brain injury journey, I found myself, literally, running into a wall at full speed. I was sitting with someone in a therapy office of some kind and we were talking about my frustration at not being able to move past something. This therapist, not a part of my regular team, looked at me and in what I heard as a condescending tone said something like, "I don't know why you are so unhappy. You are smarter now than most people will ever be."

Excuse me? Did she just ask me to settle for less and be happy about where I was at that moment? I sat, with a blank stare, trying to figure out what she meant. I was confused, but my gut told me to get out of there...to run away from anything or anyone that might hold me back. Where I was didn't have to mean this is where I would stay. Did it? I was angry, but I didn't know what I was angry about. I was insulted, but I didn't know what I was insulted by. I was the patient, she was the expert; who was I to question?

Oh, I was angry and defiant and determined. I stormed out of her office and, without slowing down, walked directly and literally into the wall, face first, just outside the door.

More tears, more frustration, less light at the end of the tunnel because of a distracted focus, divided attention, and yet another blow to my head. – Ruth

Repeat head injuries are an example of often overlooked brain injury side-effects. These incidents are not normally put in the context of the complex process of attention, but sometimes absolutely are.

Misfires in attention happen every single day and can lead to very dangerous situations.

I heard the buzz of a text message and ran a red light. -RT

I went to check the washer and left something on the stove. -DG

I was talking with a friend on the phone and forgot to pick up my child. -TR

I got distracted making coffee and did not take my medicine. -RE

I was listening to the radio and I missed a turn. -MG

I was thinking about what I was going to make for dinner, and I walked into the intersection as a car was turning the corner. -CA

Someone asked me a question while I was preparing dinner, and I cut my finger. -HS

I was reading my emails and took a large gulp of my scalding hot coffee. -MB

CHANGES IN ATTENTION

All too often, these breaks in attention are dismissed as minor, isolated, and insignificant but when you take that step back and look for patterns, the relationship between attention and safety becomes obvious.

Exercise 2 Part II: Attentional Blinks Expanded

> This exercise is for **S1 (Survivor)** and **S2 (Support)**. The directions for both are the same for both **S1 and S2.**

Choose a setting and sit with a magazine that interests you. Again, bring this workbook and pen/pencil. Open your book to this page and put the book under your magazine. Begin reading your magazine. *Every time* something pulls your attention away from your magazine, write it down in your workbook. Did you notice the bird flying by? Write it down. Did you notice a horn honking? Write it down. Did you notice that person yelling, the child's laugh, the dog's bark? Write it down. When you run out of space below, go to the next page and continue writing. Do this for 30 minutes. This time when, at the end of the day, you are reviewing what broke your attention, mark all that could have caused a problem and label it Safety (SAF). Did your shift in focus create any kind of potential safety hazard for you or anyone around you? How could this shift in focus have caused a problem? Keep in mind that a safety issue can be anything from spilling scalding hot coffee on your lap to missing an important phone call and all points in between. Again, this about identifying *any* kind of potentially negative outcome for you or those around you that resulted from an attentional blink.

Compare notes with each other.

Continue recording your observations here.

Wrap-Up

Again, the critical pieces of attentional blinks from Part I of this exercise are:

- Slow it all down,
- Figure out what is important in the scene, and
- See if a strategy to redirect focus appears.

Now, consider the impact each has on the moment. Does that attentional blink create:

- Added information or color
- Or create a safety issue?

OVERWHELM: WHEN TOO MUCH IS TOO MUCH

> *I remember the first time I walked into the dining room at the rehab center. The light felt so bright it stung my eyes. So many people. So many sounds. So many smells. I simply froze—feet in cement—I could not move. -DS*

Sensory overwhelm can stop you dead in your tracks.

We depend on our senses to piece together and process relevant information. Without thinking about it, we filter extraneous input while we are busy *doing* – whether it is the sound of the dishwasher while watching TV or the patterns the rain makes on our windshield while driving.

When we are paying careful attention and our sensory pathways are clear, we notice the amount of daily sensory input and we notice subtle changes in our processing abilities as they happen. We recognize how we need to change a strategy to better understand the world around us.

Consider this example: Imagine you are driving a car. The road is flat and dry. It is 45 degrees. The lighting is perfect. Ideal driving conditions. Now, imagine the clouds fill in, and it begins to drizzle. The temperature starts to drop. The drizzle turns to sleet and conditions change quickly. The roads get slick. The sky is dark. Perfect conditions turn to chaos in the blink of an eye.

Life changes all the time, often in subtle ways, in the blink of an eye. Your processing abilities can be working well one moment when, suddenly, one condition shifts slightly. That shift can change everything.

Sensory pathways and associated filters are frequently altered by a brain injury. That means these subtle shifts are often more dramatic in an injured brain. That process of making sense of what is happening in the world around us changes, pretty dramatically, for both survivors and support.

Our roles in life – husband, wife, mother, father, teacher, pet owner, employee or employer, etc.—are impacted, if not dictated, by our ability to pay attention and process information. Additionally, because our senses work like building blocks, a malfunction in one area can create a chaotic traffic jam in all areas.

The key to avoiding the chaos is to first dissect the situation—break it into its parts. The following is an exercise designed to help both survivor and support to figure out how to identify and separate the stream of daily sensory information.

Exercise 3 Part I: Dissecting the Situation

This exercise is for **S1 (Survivor) and S2 (Support).**

The **goal** of this exercise is to notice the extent and vast wealth of sensory information that you are processing.

Bits and pieces come through your sight, hearing, taste, touch, and smell every moment of every day. Take a few minutes out of your day, and notice all the varied sensory information you process at any given moment.

Pick a moment in your day and freeze time. What do you see? What do you hear? What do you taste? What do you feel (sense of touch)? What do you smell?

On the lines below: Record every bit of sensory information you are receiving in that moment of time.

See:

Hear:

Taste:

Touch:

Smell:

Wrap-up

From this exercise, you might have noticed the wealth of sensory information that your brain is constantly processing. Now consider how much of that information your brain is filtering and processing *without* your conscious effort. That's a lot of work.

When you break all of this down into its parts it is very easy to see how a brain injury can create chaos and overwhelm.

Why is it so important to be able to focus on understanding sensory information? First and foremost, it is about **safety**.

- *Does that change in **taste** indicate spoiled food that might make you sick?*
- *Can you distinguish the **smell** of a gas leak?*
- *Are you able to determine when a surface is too hot to **touch** safely?*
- *Can you **hear** the car coming up behind you in the parking lot?*
- *Do you **see** the child on a skateboard out of the corner of your eye?*

Next, it is about understanding, making sense of the world, and maintaining a good **quality of life**.

- *Do you **taste** the flavors that awaken your palate?*
- *When you walk in the house, can you **smell** the cookies baking in the oven?*
- *Can you enjoy the **touch** and comfort of your child's hand in yours?*
- *Can you **hear** the subtle changes in tone of voice?*
- *Are you able to **see** and read the words in your favorite passage of a book?*

Exercise 3 Part II: Assign Importance

This exercise is for both **S1 (Survivor) and S2 (Support).** The directions are the same for both **S1 and S2.**

The **goal** of this exercise is be aware of the consequences of attentional blinks.

Let's revisit the previous exercise to put it all in perspective.

For this exercise you will need colored pencils, pens, or crayons.

Choose two different colors: one to signify a quality of life issue and one to signify a safety issue.

Go back through that previous workbook page and with each entry ask yourself *so what.* For example, if your dissected situation was a conversation with a friend and you identified that your sweater was itchy, ask yourself *so what* to help identify a quality of life versus a safety issue. Here is a possible way this internal dialogue might go:

So what: So it is distracting me.
So what: So I can't pay attention to what is being said.
So what: So I start to fall behind in the conversation.
So what: So then I start to feel stupid and lost.

This is quality of life issue. Circle it with your quality of life colored pencil.

Compare notes and review with each other. Are differences in how you assessed the importance of the situation? Talk it through.

Wrap-up

Your senses both keep us alive and help us live. Your safety is dependent upon understanding and incorporating our sensory information. However, from this exercise you may have noticed that your senses also fill in the details of the moment making them richer, more colorful, more multidimensional, and so much more interesting. Sensory information adds quality and beauty to life.

Now What?

Once you understand how to break sensory information into its parts, you start to get a better picture of how you can stop sensory overwhelm from happening and start filling your life with strategies to shift from chaos to understanding.

I used to walk into a room with a cellphone plastered to my ear, trying to appear as if I was in deep conversation. –RS

I started out sitting in the very front of the classroom but the professor tried to make eye contact and that set off the flood of sounds – paper crinkling, people breathing, lights buzzing, pencils moving across the paper. Now I find a spot at the far side of the room. Where I melt into the background, I can focus better. –CA

I can see the expression on his face change when everything is just too much to handle. I have tried many things—anything that will take his attention away from everything swimming around in his head and move it to something, anything else. –BM

My mom gets overwhelmed in public by all that is going on around her. My best tool is to find something out of the ordinary, like a street performer, to distract, grab her attention, and break that overwhelm. –LW

One of the best ways to cope with that chaos is to use another sense or a distraction to break the tension and shift your attention.

Exercise 4: Recognizing the Signs

The following is an exercise for both **S1 (Survivor)** and **S2 (Support)**. NOTE: **S1** and **S2** will **not** be following the same directions. To get the most of out of this exercise be sure to compare notes at the end of each day.

The **goal** of this exercise is to become aware of conditions that can trigger a sensory overwhelm.

On any given day, you may be finding yourself in a situation that causes you to react in an unfamiliar way. Learning to recognize the signs that may trigger a reaction helps you regain your control.

For both **S1** and **S2,** this is a 5 day exercise. On the next page you will find a Recognizing the Signs Worksheet. There are four more in the Appendix starting on page 189.

For **S1,** at the end of each day, choose 2 different situations to record: one where you felt in control and one where you felt out of control. Record as many details as you can, paying careful attention to the sensory information and how you were feeling. What physical or emotional signs did you notice when you felt overwhelmed? What environment or situation felt comfortable? Record all the clues that will help you identify any triggers that caused sensory overwhelm. Again, do this exercise every day for five days to help identify patterns.

For **S2,** on day one, you will follow the same directions as above. On days 2-5, shift your perspective and move into the role as the observer. What did you notice? Were you able to identify any triggers in **S1**? Did you notice any patterns?

At the end of each day, compare notes.

RECOGNIZING THE SIGNS WORKSHEET

Details of the situation #1:

What happened when you started to feel overwhelm?

Details of the situation #2:

What happened when you started to feel overwhelm?

Wrap-up

This is a very powerful exercise for several reasons.

For the survivor:
- It helps you recognize that there are situations and environmental conditions that trigger overwhelm.
- It helps you recognize that there are often clues that come before the overwhelm.

For the support:
- As for the survivor, it helps you recognize that there are situations and environmental conditions that trigger overwhelm and helps you recognize that there are often clues that come before the overwhelm.
- It is also the first real peek inside the injured brain. That helps build empathy and understanding which in turn will help build a stronger partnership.

Sensory overwhelm can happen at any time and, when it does, that wave can knock you down and pull you under.

Regardless of where you are on your recovery journey, it is important to recognize what triggers overwhelm and how that feels.

Recognizing and isolating those situations that feel overwhelming can help you better understand how to deal with what comes next. Ask yourself:

- Am I comfortable in this environment?
- Am I thinking clearly?
- How does my body feel? Is there any tension building in my muscles or am I relaxed?
- Are any of my senses peaking?
- What options do I have?

CHANGES IN ATTENTION

Think about a situation where everything felt like too much—too many noises, too many smells, too much light, too many people. From a distance, take a look back and try to identify the things you could have had control of within that environment. How could you rescript that scene to make it more comfortable? What elements, events, or choices could you have changed to stop the overwhelm?

Exercise 5: Rescripting

This exercise is for **S1 (Survivor) and S2 (Support).** The directions are the same for both **S1 and S2** however, see below for additional directions for **S2.**

The **goal** of this exercise is to begin working as partners in healing and identify alternatives when faced with sensory overwhelm.

In this exercise, using **S1's** workbook page, select three scenarios they identified as overwhelming, and move each to this page in the space below, one item to each box. Look at each scenario and, together, write out how you could rescript that experience. In essence, how could you, together, create a less stressful outcome? For example, could you have moved a different part of the room—one that was less noisy or bright or crowded or cold? Could either of you done something to break the tension or redirect attention to ease the situation?

Compare notes with each other.

Experience 1 Summary:

Experience 1 Rescripting:

Experience 2 Summary:

Experience 2 Rescripting:

Experience 3 Summary:

Experience 3 Rescripting:

Wrap-up

In this exercise you might have found that you deepened your understanding of triggers and identified actions you can take, next time, in the moment, to head off overwhelm.

When you are able to look at situations together and problem solve as a team, you open the door to understanding and begin to move forward as partners in healing.

Recognizing we have choices is empowering, even if that recognition comes in hindsight. Sometimes, the smallest changes in behavior or decisions can affect your quality of life by easing a situation from chaos to calm.

Self-care, Self-love: Recognize, Act, and Celebrate

Part of my job as a puppy raiser for Guide Dogs for the Blind is to socialize the puppies in appropriate environments. Starbucks, with all its smells and activity, is the perfect environment for puppies when they are young. One day my husband and I went to Starbucks with our three-month old puppy-in-training.

Here's my regular Starbucks routine: I walk in, go to the counter, settle the puppy, and then I place my order. On that day, there was no room to move after placing my order. Add that to a lack of light, packed house, and a non-service dog sitting so close to the counter—powder keg of emotion building and building. While my focus was still on settling the puppy, the clerk kept pushing me to move faster, and for the second time in 30 seconds, asked me for my order. As I reached to get out my loyalty card, I said, "I need a moment" and that fell on deaf ears as the harried clerk examined the line growing behind me. I felt the connections, those that give me a sense of control, start to fail as the chaos began to creep into my brain and muddy the channels. Again she pushed for my order. I felt the tension build in my muscles – jaw clenched, fist on the leash growing tighter, knot growing in my stomach. I knew that the volume was turning up in my head, amplifying every sensation and I knew I needed to do something. I recognized that I was about to hit that point where the chaos consumed me and that I was almost too far in the wave that would pull me under. I needed to regain control.

I took a step back from the counter, squared my feet, took a long, deep breath, and when she pressed one more time for my order, I established eye contact and said, firmly "I'm doing the best I can. I need a moment."

That stopped the wave and I was back in control. - Mary

These situations come up every day – most days, multiple times. It is not uncommon for the wave of overwhelm to grab you and take you under.

The important take-away in this scenario is that when you recognize those moments as they are happening and act to control them, it is critical to celebrate the victories. That is the starting point for firmly establishing what feels manageable, on your terms.

Knowing what you can and can't control helps you reclaim ownership of your moments. Next time this comes up, you might even recognize the feelings faster, allowing you to catch the overwhelm sooner, saving you time and energy.

The other key piece is that, initially, not all wins are *big wins*. Mini-wins, like this one, where you regain your balance in the moment, add up and become big wins. Learning to recognize and accept, one moment at time, the way life is right now, empowers you to take small steps forward.

Journal

Creating mini-wins is like practicing a golf swing – the only way to get your swing perfect is to repeat the same motion, over and over – you are creating muscle memory. The more you practice, the more natural the process becomes, and the more likely you are to repeat it in the moment. Remember, mini-wins create big wins.

*Reflect on a moment you felt was a mini-win. What does that feel like? Now think about how you can create mini-wins, more often. Sometimes it is as simple as figuring out what you can and can't control. Take a few minutes and write out what a mini-win means and feels like **to you**, and you how might create more.*

Is Attention Something We Can Summon?

The answer, briefly, is yes; but this is not the whole story. The ability to summon attention changes after a brain injury. Strategies that may have worked previously may no longer work as well or at all.

Keep in mind, our ability to summon attention is conditional—it depends on what is happening around us. "Just focus!" is a frequent battle cry of all parties involved.

Sometimes, no matter how hard we try, we cannot filter out extraneous sensory noise and summon our ability to pay attention. For example, if you are sitting at your kitchen table trying to read an article in the paper and the guy next door fires up his chainsaw, it is quite difficult to summon your focus and pay attention to what is in front of you.

In order to summon attention and have it work properly, you need to manage your environment.

Attention is affected by so many factors. How well you process information is affected by the number of variables you have to filter—those things that are both within and outside our control.

Here are some ways to manage some of those variables and reduce extraneous sensory noise:

- Remove clutter.
- Limit light. Close the drapes. Change the light source (fluorescent lights, lamp light, LED lights all have different effects on how well you see).
- Reduce the number of people in the room or move to a place where there are fewer people.
- Be mindful of how your clothing feels on your skin. If it is irritating, change it.
- Use earplugs or earphones to reduce noise distractions.
- Bring in fresh air if a smell is bothering you.

CHAPTER NINE
The Bridge From Attention to Cognitive Functioning

The connection between attention and cognitive function seems so obvious, and, in many ways, it is. Cognitive function requires attention and our ability to pay attention requires cognitive function. It is when we look at the deeper roots of the connection between the two that we realize the shared space is what allows us to become aware of and understand what is going on around us.

One brain process can be found right at the intersection of attention and cognitive functioning and so closely links the two that, at a point, they become inseparable—memory.

Memory is typically considered a three-step process: encoding (translating raw information into a form the brain can handle and understand), storing (categorizing, synthesizing, and filing away the information for later use), and retrieving (recalling and producing information at the right time).

We, however, believe that the traditional view of the process skips the most important step—the one that makes the process possible—attention. The memory process can't start until you pay attention.

Think about this sobering notion as a reality check:

You have 0% chance of remembering something you do not or did not pay attention to.

And, if you do not notice something as it is happening, that piece of information cannot be encoded for storage, which means, of course, that you can't reasonably expect to remember it later. With this in mind, every exercise in the previous section was, in essence, a memory exercise. Memory starts and ends with attention.

That fact sheds a whole new light on how to look at where memory breaks down and brings into clarity the root of all difficulties with memory post brain injury.

Here is how we will visualize the memory process.

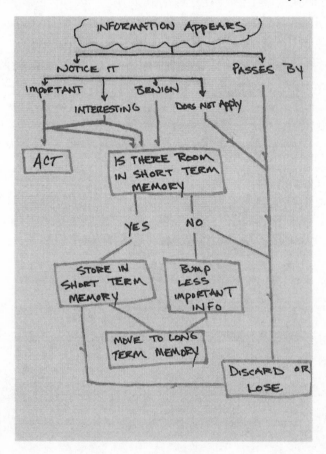

This slightly different way of looking at the process makes so much more sense when considering what happens post brain injury. Take a good look at that flow chart. Explore some of the places where the memory process can fail.

Now, consider the real-life impact:

On my way into the grocery store I was busy thinking about finding my list, making sure I had my wallet, putting my keys in a compartment in my backpack where I'd find them later, checking to make sure my cellphone ringer was turned on, and trying not to get hit by a car in the busy parking lot. I did not pay attention to where I parked my car. -RS

I was focused on a phone call and did not even notice that my co-worker put a note on my desk asking me to come to the conference room for a meeting. I didn't "forget" the meeting. I had no idea there even was one. -CM

I made two dozen cookies for a bake sale at my son's school. Apparently, someone told me last week that it was cancelled, but I guess I was not paying attention. Sadly, I had to eat all of the cookies by myself. -DJ

I was sitting in the waiting room at a doctor's office and a child, on the other side of the room burst out laughing. I missed the nurse calling my name. I just sat there as people looked around the room. -GL

In the last section we discussed attentional blinks—those shiny things that tug and pull on your attention and, in a flash, cause you to shift focus and lose track of important information happening around you.

Now consider what happens to those pieces of information that simply slide right past you without you noticing them at all, either because they are not relevant at that moment or they are simply lost in the sea of information around you. It does not matter where or how the information was lost, it will not stand a chance of being encoded and therefore will never enter the memory process.

Few things can throw you off your game more than feeling like you are forgetting things. It is beyond unsettling to believe that lapses in memory fail not just yourself but those around you.

A statement of life is: pre- or post brain injury, there is no way you will notice everything. Once you recognize that you can't possible notice everything, some of that discomfort will ease.

Journal

A statement of life is: pre- or post brain injury, there is no way you will notice everything. Once you recognize that you can't possible notice everything some of the discomfort associated with that feeling that you are forgetting things, will ease.

Give yourself permission to **not** notice everything. Take a minute to write out how that feels when you give yourself permission to miss something, omitting it from memory.

_____

_____

_____

_____

_____

_____

_____

_____

_____

_____

_____

CHAPTER TEN

Changes In Thinking: Cognitive Processing

Changes in cognitive processing bring about one of life's greatest transitions—one that no one prepares for. It is not a job change, marital change, or relocation—those, in most cases, we prepare for. A brain injury brings about a sudden, unanticipated condition that touches every part of our lives because it affects how we live in the world.

I pulled into a space in the parking garage and turned off the car. The key would not come out…. No matter how many ways I pushed and pulled, it would not budge—I just couldn't figure out what to do. In tears, I called home and a calm, reasonable voice walked me through all the possible reasons the key would not come out. We got to "Is the car in Park" and I shook my head, slid the stick shift to park, and removed the key. I needed help, for a very long time, troubleshooting the little things in life. —Ruth

It is often the mundane tasks—those that require seemingly simple problem-solving skills—that trip you up after a brain injury and create the biggest roadblocks to navigating life.

I remember Jim standing in front of the washing machine, filled with clothes, lid up, just looking at it. "What's up, honey?" "It won't start." I gently closed the lid and said "Now try it." He pushed the Start button and the machine did its magic. –JE

The way you process pieces of information and the way you put those pieces together to create a meaningful picture often change. The ability to find the right word, complete a task from start to finish in the right order, solve a problem, understand a joke, or even remember appointments is dictated by cognitive abilities. The once comfortable and almost automatic process of putting information together is different and sometimes unfamiliar after a brain injury.

The whole concept of cognitive functioning, and all its parts, is huge. It is so big that recognizing subtle changes is often lost in initial assessment.

Can you name the date?
Who is the current president?
Tell me where you were born.
Where are you right now?
Please count backwards from 10.
Read this passage out loud.
What did you have for dinner last night?

Cognitive functioning includes so much more than these simple questions can cover. To understand just how broad and all encompassing this area of brain function is, consider this general definition of cognitive functioning:

> ***Cognitive functioning****: Brain activities that lead to knowledge and understanding. Includes all means and mechanisms of acquiring information. Encompasses perception, reasoning, language, and memory.*

Think about this: The brain is always working. Outside of those physical processes that regulate the body's survival systems—heart rate, breathing, digestion—everything else involves cognitive processing. Even the active intention of not thinking—of clearing your mind and consciously calming brain activity—*is* a cognitive process.

For our purposes, we will accept these two critical pieces of this puzzle as fact:

- **First,** regardless of the location and type of brain injury, cognitive processing will be affected to some degree.
  - One constant when looking at brain injury as a whole is that there is no reasonable way to make generalizations about changes in cognitive functioning in terms of quality or degree. Regardless of type and location, brain injury, by definition, affects thinking processes, or, cognitive functioning.

- **Second,** and what we will look at in greater detail, changes in cognitive functioning—how we gather information, how we think, how we perceive, how we understand what is happening—impact how we see ourselves and the world around us. For better or worse, those changes in cognitive functioning also impact how others see us.
  - These changes, in turn, can alter how successfully we navigate daily life and our relationships.

QUALITY OF LIFE MATTERS!

Go back to the definition of cognitive functioning and re-read it. Let's break down how all of this fits together and why it is important for both survivors and their support system to understand.

In general, this definition breaks into two parts: acquiring information *and* interpreting, understanding, and processing that information.

Let's start with what it means to **acquire information**. In its simplest form, *acquiring information* is fact finding. Period. You *acquire information* every moment of every day, both actively and passively. It is those automatic and intentional processes—the ones that allow you to gather pieces of data from your experience of the world around you—that make it possible for you to understand what is happening and what you need to know. In this context, *acquiring information* is not about making decisions. *Acquiring information* is about gathering all the facts to make those decisions. It is your body's way of doing research, much like looking something up in a book or even taking a class. In the context of cognitive functioning, *acquiring information* is all about the pieces— what you see, how your skin feels, the temperature of the air as it hits your lungs, smells, sounds, what you know from previous experience, etc.—that allow you to make sense of the world.

The second piece of cognitive functioning that we will discuss here encompasses how you interpret, understand and order the information that you acquire. That involves aspects of thinking (*perception, reasoning, language, and memory*) and sequencing (the ability to break down actions into manageable units and prioritize them in the right order).

Perception is the spin you put on that information—how you interpret and assign meaning to the bits and pieces. That interpretation is based on what you know, what you have experienced before, and how you believe everything fits together. Changes in *perception,* whether those are intentional or not, can also alter how you pay attention to what is going on around you and how you physically and emotionally interact with the world and others. Though it is often dismissed as mere opinion, *perception* forms the frame around everything you *see* and is critical to how you act and react in any given moment.

Reasoning is the process that allows us to take facts and put them together in a logical way. Much like the integration processes of *perception, reasoning* allows you to assemble the bits

82

and pieces of information logically so that you can draw conclusions and make decisions. That said, changes in *reasoning* alter how you make decisions about how to act and react, which, in turn, shifts how others interact with you.

Language, in this context, is so much bigger than the word conveys. *Language* is the verbal *and* non-verbal system that you use to interpret communication and express yourself. That encompasses all the nuances and contexts including processing things like humor, sarcasm, cultural expressions, slang, etc. *Language* is the foundation of how you interact with yourself and others. What appears to be the biggest issue with *language* post brain injury is word-finding. That struggle to find the right word or phrase to express a thought or condition can be confounding.

Sequencing is the step-by-step process you use to put order into your thoughts and life. It is the ability to break down both simple and complex thoughts and tasks into manageable bites before putting those pieces back together in the most effective order.

Again, a brain injury brings about a sudden, unanticipated condition that touches every part of life because it affects how you live in the world.

Keep in mind that every exercise in this book is really a cognitive exercise. Unlike any other part of this book, the exercises in this section are intended to make you aware that there is a process behind thinking—**we want you to pay attention to and understand what is actually happening when you think.**

Once you are aware of what is going on behind the scenes, you can better understand both the process of thinking and where you might have a few gaps in your cognitive abilities. We believe that every thought has a process and every process has alternatives.

What that means is that when a cognitive process breaks down, **your brain has options.** The goal of these exercises is to help explore some options—try a few on to see how they fit. You will, with experience, find the workarounds that serve you best.

Exercise 6: Acquiring Information

> This is a team exercise for **S1 (Survivor)** and **S2 (Support)**.
>
> The **goal** of this exercise is to isolate and notice sensory information.

This is a two person, guided exercise and offers both S1 and S2 insight into the volumes of information you are constantly, actively and passively, processing every minute of every day.

Find a place that offers a large amount of varied sensory input. Some examples include: the cosmetics department in a large department store, the deli department in a grocery store, or a restaurant.

Find a place where you can safely stand or sit with your eyes closed for several minutes. Whether you are sitting or standing, make sure both of your feet are firmly planted on the ground.

In this guided exercise one person will read the following completely—leading the other through step by step. When you are finished, switch roles.

- Close your eyes and take a slow, gentle deep breath. Feel the rush of cool air as it enters through your nostrils. Now exhale and feel the warmth of your breath as it slowly and easily leaves your mouth.
- Take in another breath through your nose. What do you smell? Describe everything you smell – each scent – in detail whether that is food or trees or diesel fuel, try to isolate and smell each scent as it comes into your awareness.

- Now focus on your skin. Do you feel warm or cool? Dry or damp? Is something touching your skin – maybe a shirt or sweater? Try to zero in on how your skin feels in this moment.

- Shift your focus to sounds in the environment. Separate all the sounds. Try to isolate each and experience it. Describe each of those sounds and identify how they make you feel. Are they loud or jarring or calming or confusing? Break everything you hear down and focus on the individual sounds.

- Now lick your lips. What do you taste? Describe what you taste in this moment. Does that bring up any images in your mind? Focus on the taste on your lips and those thoughts that go with it.

- Now, with your eyes still closed, try to put all that sensory information together and see, in your mind's eye, the whole picture with all the pieces filled in.

Make this part of your weekly routine by practicing this exercise in a variety of environments.

This will awaken your senses and enhance your quality of life while you open pathways and make new connections in your brain.

Wrap-up

When you pause and become aware of how much information is swirling around you, you can appreciate just how much happens, cognitively, without you even noticing.

The point of this exercise is to make you aware of the volumes of information you are receiving, passively and actively, at any given point in time. More often than not, you filter this information seamlessly, sifting and sorting by relevance as the moment happens. Your actions and reactions are based on this information, in context.

Acquiring information is a much more complex process than it appears on the surface. In order to live effectively, it is important to process all the new information—blend it, compare it, and synthesize it—with old information (what you know or have experienced). Then, you form a plan to either save, discard, or act on that new information—all in less than a blink of an eye.

Now, take a minute and revisit the exercise on page (Dissecting the Situation exercise) and see how it felt to intentionally direct your attention. Think about how much other information was actually there, just swirling, that you filtered out.

Exercise 7: Word Order

This exercise is for **S1 (Survivor)** and **S2 (Support).**

The **goal** of this exercise is to strengthen both word finding and order through practice.

In this exercise you will create sentences using the words listed below. Use as few or as many words as you wish. There is no one right answer in this exercise. The key is to create sentences that make sense to you.

Choose words and practice building 3-10 sentences per session.

man	run	green
car	skip	fast
dog	chew	hot
telephone	sniff	tall
you	talk	big
girl	taste	sweet
parent	hug	cold
book	read	long
table	set	square
friend	call	nice
library	is	open
horses	are	friendly
worms	were	slow
go/going	far	quiet
I	am	happy
very	the	and
quickly	a	but
quietly	an	or
never	nor	yet

You can also make this an interactive game. Write these words and any other words you would like to add on index cards and place the cards on the middle of the table. Set a timer for three minutes. See who can complete the most sentences before time runs out.

Write your sentences below.

Wrap-up

This playful exercise is the perfect example of where areas of cognitive functioning overlap. The exercise may appear to be about language, words, and understanding, but it is also about following steps, maintaining logical order, and reasoning.

In reality, you are working two very distinct cognitive processes. The first is *reasoning*: the act of putting thoughts and actions together in a logical, sensible way.

The second is *sequencing*: that process that allows us to complete tasks from start to finish in the most effective order.

You may see the order of the words differently at different times and that is perfectly fine. The goal is to create logic out of chaos—in this case, a jumble of words—and move forward. Find the logical order, whatever makes sense to you.

Exercise 8: The Steps in a Process

This exercise is for **S1 (Survivor)** and **S2 (Support)**.

The **goal** of this exercise is to strengthen sequencing skills (order) again, through practice.

The purpose of this exercise is to slow down and think through all the steps in a simple process. Slowing down allows us to think about all of the separate steps involved in the most routine daily tasks.

For each task listed below, write out every step involved, from start to successful completion, from start to finish. Be specific and thorough. If you are having a hard time starting or thinking about any of these, take out the materials you need to actually perform that task and do it. Write down each step.

Task 1: Make a hard boiled egg.

Task 2: Receive the electric bill. Write the steps you must take from the moment you receive the bill through payment of that bill.

Task 3: Make a PB&J sandwich.

Task 4: Set an appointment with the doctor.

Possible solutions for each of the scenarios is included in the appendix (page 193) along with a list of additional tasks for practice. This is one of those skills that does get better with practice.

Wrap-up

This exercise is another great example of where areas of cognitive functioning overlap. You are using logic, problem solving, memory, and language with a goal in mind.

The more you practice this skill, the more you will recognize the importance of each step in even the simplest processes. Repetition will allow you to slow down and understand how to break it all down to solve problems (big and small) and complete daily tasks. It makes you more aware of just how often order is important.

Challenges with sequencing can not only create stumbling blocks and frustration post brain injury, they can pose a safety hazard. Take a look at the steps you listed for making a hard boiled egg. Did you include "Turn off the stove" as part of your process? Think about what might happen if you did not.

Exercise 9: Word Search

> This exercise is for **S1 (Survivor)** and **S2 (Support)**.
>
> The **goal** of this exercise is to practice word finding and searching and sorting while having some fun.

These are classic word search puzzles with a twist. In each puzzle, you will be finding synonyms for the identified word.

Other Ways to Say **Annoyed**

```
d d c h i d x b o i p o o d h
f i o l y y o o c r a o d l g
k i s w x t w b s r p i e e h
i c d p h q k y u i d g j s f
y w b e l w z w p t u x l g y
i v r i k e h y l a v g v q w
z e j i n o a j n t c l x c w
d x k d n b v s d e a j u t j
u z l n k f l o e d g c e x s
d e n e d d a m r d u s s n u
h k y y p h k r e p p g d p a
u z z p h f m o g u z n n z n
s v m z z f v o n k x k g l p
d y d o h n f z a i q m s w f
f r u s t r a t e d p b a p b
```

angered	upset
bothered	provoked
displeased	maddened
frustrated	irritated

Other Ways to Say **HAPPY**

```
h n j s d t o c y k h c z j j
h s q f z z i f w c m z t d q
d h y r y t u j s c t m s f f
a e h c a x e u f l v s m m p
w p t t l w y e v u u j n d b
f j s h s z o e y f w o m n t
f c w l g d a p v r r g h j d
e o m e f i c f l e u p e o f
w q l l d h l d k e o d l y r
c o n t e n t e e h a f r f z
t j t e c k m h d c e s h u p
e h r v o v c p a j x e e l m
i y y l u l x x o r q o j d p
h q o z j z z o l m i e x r g
a d a l g v v i i j a p d f s
```

cheerful	pleased
cheery	joyful
content	glad
delighted	ecstatic

Other Ways to Say **COLD**

```
f r o s t y w u y k q g g g r
j u t h l n p i s c i z v n m
y f x l d b m m n w i g i i m
k h i o i e m x l t a u c z s
h h j t f i v z d k r g x e z
c f t d o k h g s r c y i e q
n e z o r f h z o a t c s r a
r p v q j q m l v x i y j f i
y u o y p h v u c x c u s c s
z r d i k b d w j p l l l c w
p u t e g o p p q u c u t g j
c x z b s l o z k b w w n v i
c z c a f t z b a k s s q e x
c e x z n d m e e r q o q m q
j c s m o n z k p c e j s f t
```

arctic   wintry
bitter   icy
chilly   frozen
freezing   frosty

97

Other Ways to Say **KIND**

```
n d v w y e u g k g e c w j c
c w s e n b e n p x n p h o j
j o y a y c l t k x j i n w r
j d m b o m t y o u x s r p h
w u p p i q n e e n i v q a x
h e a u a g e r i d f q w y c
y u t x v s g o e j y m g o v
r q h z b u s r e v h x q k a
q w e t k q a i s q j c o u c
n n t h q t z k o j r f p f y
j o i h e n i c e n h v a u o
e z c g i o r o f l a u h c d
b v l u f t h g u o h t v c w
k d f n w v h g y z z y e r t
x s d g u b k r e d r q h e v
```

sympathetic   caring
compassionate   thoughtful
considerate   nice
Gentle   humane

Wrap-up

This type of puzzle is yet another excellent example of a cross-over exercise. You are working multiple cognitive and attention processes all at once. This specific exercise, one where all of the words you are finding in each puzzle convey different ways to say the same thing, can remind you that there are many, many ways to express a thought. There is no one right word or phrase and sometimes alternatives will help you get past that word-finding block.

Journal

Take a few minutes and think about the exercises you completed in this section. Which, if any, exercise(s) were easy for you? Do you know why? Which, if any, were challenging? Which ones were fun and felt like play? Again, can you identify why?

_____

_____

_____

_____

_____

_____

_____

_____

_____

_____

_____

_____

_____

CHAPTER ELEVEN
The Bridge Between Changes in Cognitive Functioning and Emotional Control

Changes in thinking, in many cases, are woven so tightly within the fabric of changes in emotional control that, much like the strong link between attention and cognitive functioning, it is almost impossible to separate them. We will look at two highly related functions here—language and self-concept—that have vast implications for survivors and support and can alter the course of healing in both subtle and direct ways.

Words and language are our vehicles to express what is happening in our lives and in our thinking. With that it mind, it's pretty obvious that being able to communicate effectively is critical to daily life. During recovery and rebuilding, it is essential to be able to put a thought into a form that someone else will understand. That way, they can see what is happening inside the injured brain.

The Power of Words and Finding the Right Ones

In the exercises from the two previous sections—Changes in Attention and Changes in Cognitive Functioning—you might have noticed how communication, both verbal and nonverbal, has the power to trigger all-consuming emotions. The inability to find the right way to say something—those exact words to convey the full meaning—coupled with how that message is received and interpreted can lead to feelings of defeat, frustration, and isolation.

Language and communication can be sources of great frustration for those navigating an injured brain. After a brain injury, an inability to express and interpret words, body language, and tone of voice, all in context, can become an incredibly vicious cycle. When you struggle to find the words or your tone is colored by physical pain or frustration, communication breaks down and can leave you feeling disconnected from yourself and others. Your support system can't possibly see or understand the battle that is waging in your head and, therefore, might misinterpret *your* language, deepening that miscommunication.

Think about the vicious cycle of trying to say something that is not coming out right. It looks something like this:

> You're in conversation with a friend and struggle to find the right words to express your thoughts. You work to clarify but can't come up with another way to say what you want to say. No words. You push to keep unrelated factors like pain, exhaustion, or overload from creeping into that message through your body language and tone of voice. You try other words and, still, you miss the mark and are unable to convey what is bubbling up in your thoughts. Communication breaks down, emotions take over, and the message is lost.

That sequence of events starts the cycle of missed communication and interpretations that just don't adequately match the intended message. That can lead to frustration and frustration can lead to either anger or shutting down.

Both anger and shutting down tend to exaggerate both miscommunication and misunderstanding. And so, the cycle continues….

Self Concept

Self concept—how you define and see yourself—is another of those big overlapping issues and often is reflected in the words you choose to describe who you are, coloring the impressions that you leave.

I'm motivated.
I'm organized.
I multi-task well.
I'm a people-person.
I'm funny.
I'm an anchor, the glue that holds everyone together.

When self-concept does not reflect parts of your new, post-brain injury reality, a state referred to as *cognitive dissonance* is created.

Cognitive dissonance: *the state of psychological discomfort that comes from recognizing a gaping divide between what is real (how you are really functioning post brain injury) and what you believe about yourself.*

In the context of an injured brain, *cognitive dissonance* takes on a different twist. What you know to be true about who you are, how you define yourself, and how you expect that self to act often don't match how you are dealing with the world from inside your changed brain. When reality does not match—when all the facts are telling you that these traits no longer define how you are acting and reacting today—an internal struggle is experienced, one that must be mediated and resolved to create peace. Cognitive dissonance is not a healing place nor is it healthy to live with for any extended period of time. You must work to find ways to bridge that gaping divide.

The more deeply personal the belief, the greater the feelings of unease and the more that dissonance can rock your self-confidence, self-esteem, and, sometimes, self-worth. For example, someone who has always defined themselves as intelligent may struggle to hold onto that self-concept when they can't solve simple problems or find the right words. That cognitive dissonance is uncomfortable and is not a productive or positive place to live.

Loss of Self

A brain injury can create a loss of self. A loss of self *is* real. Grief is the avenue to heal that loss. Letting go is a process—in its own way, a mourning process—but one that must happen in order to move forward.

There is a progression from blame to acceptance to embracing who you are that allows you to stop comparing the old you and step into who you are right now. That is a cognitive process—one that requires you to think about your emotions and your emotional reactions. It is a rebuilding, a reorganizing, and a restructuring—starting from scratch.

The Hidden Grief

There is an element that often goes unnoticed, unacknowledged, and dismissed: the grief experienced by those closest to the survivor.

I was so caught up in the process of caring and being supportive, I didn't have time to process how I was feeling. I didn't think about my emotions. It was so sudden. It's not like a disease where you have time to adjust to the changes in that person. I just wanted to help in any way I could. I went from being a daughter to a caregiver overnight, and because I was home I was the translator when others came home, responsible for explaining mom's behavior and struggles. Two years had passed before I realized I never gave myself permission to mourn the reality that the mom I once knew was not the mom I was looking at now. But, so much time had passed, I wondered if it was still OK to grieve, but the tears were already flowing. –Mary's daughter

Support often feels the guilt associated with putting themselves first—they are supposed to be caregivers and supportive. They may silently scold, "How dare I feel grief, loss, and despair! I should just be grateful my loved one is here." The feelings of mourning the loss of someone once known can be further compounded by guilt over a perceived lack of gratitude.

The survivor, that person they love, is still there and still needs support. But, that person is not there, not as they once were, and there is work to be done with little time left for the emotions of loss.

Grief feels oh so selfish and sometimes poorly timed. However, whether two days, two months, two years, or even longer has passed, it is important to note, there is no time frame for the mourning and grieving process for both support and survivor.

Redefining Self-Concept

My friend said to me "You can't multi-task like you used to." My initial reaction was to move to emotional recovery mode, responding with "You are right, I can't." With that statement, I felt like I was both accepting my changes and working hard to reverse them. I realized, however, that instead of looking back, I need to look forward, emphasizing my strengths in the current moment and finding the beauty in who I am now. Wallowing in what used to be no longer serves me and I continually work to stop apologizing for how I changed.   –Ruth

At some point it is no longer about the mourning and grieving process. It is about moving beyond the blame. There comes a point where the most important and productive thing you can do is stop giving power to your brain injury and look at who you are, *not* who you were.

Remember....

Seeing who you are today is powerful.
Who you are is exactly who you need to be.
This moment is the perfect place to begin.
You have the power to modify how you see yourself and start
to find that comfortable place to live.

The Shared Journey

Consider this: The more you, survivor and support, blame the brain injury, the more weight you give to the fact that there is something wrong. That gives all your power to the injury or the diagnosis and takes away your ability to live comfortably with who you are today and find what is right.

Today I will appreciate what I can do and how well I do it.
Today I replace apology with acceptance so that I can embrace what is working in this moment.
Today I will begin to reclaim that power.

Today what will you do?

Journal

Think about how you look at your brain injury and how it has changed you. Are you giving it power? Is that power holding you back? How can you break that cycle? Bookmark this page. This self-reflection is critical and you will want to come back to this page and add more ideas and thoughts as they come to you.

_____

_____

_____

_____

_____

_____

_____

_____

_____

_____

_____

_____

CHAPTER TWELVE
Changes in Emotional Control

I remember standing in the kitchen with my teenage daughter. I had just snapped and overreacted to something trivial, something insignificant. She told me I was not the mom she grew up with. Her patient mom was not there anymore. She was struggling because she didn't know which mom would be there reacting in that moment—was it patient mom or the one that was set off by the smallest things? That continues to be one of the most difficult and heart wrenching challenges that I face, and the reason that I now sometimes even catch myself before losing my cool. - Mary

Two days after the accident I was sitting at my desk when the phone rang. It was a radio talk show host and, as part of my job, I was supposed to make sure that everyone who was recording commercials felt happy and well cared for. The host wanted a script change, which 3 days earlier I would have made happen without a blink, all while wearing a big smile. However, this wasn't 3 days before. The minute she started to squawk, I froze and hung up the phone. I said nothing to her. I just hung up. I thought I could pretend we were disconnected and then restart the conversation. My boss, the owner of the agency, whose desk was right next to mine, looked on in horror. She looked me right in the eye and sent me home. She said "something is wrong...you need to go home."

She didn't fire me, but she realized the "people person" I once was, was gone. - Ruth

Perhaps the most difficult area to explore and understand is in relation to changes in our reactions. It is all too easy and common to jump to the conclusion that someone's core personality has changed as a result of a brain injury. In reality, what the rest of the world is seeing is a change in how the survivor reacts on an emotional level, not a change to their core personality.

That is important for several reasons. First, it is critical for all parties involved to know that changes **do** happen and those changes **will** affect relationships. Second, it is crucial to remember that it is easier to change an emotional reaction than a personality trait.

Personality—the core of who we are—evolves over our lifespan. Dramatic changes don't happen in an instant. Shifts after a brain injury are more likely tied to how we manage our emotions. How about some examples to help?

- Stubbornness is a personality trait. Picking an argument is an emotional response.
- When you call someone "kind," you are describing a personality trait. When you hear someone making a nice comment, you are noticing an emotional response.

- Having an optimistic outlook on life is a personality trait.

112

Being happy about winning a game is an emotional response.

- Impatience is a personality trait. Getting angry because life got bumpy is an emotional response.
- Extroversion is a personality trait. Choosing to participate in social functions is an emotional response.
- Having a good sense of humor is a personality trait. Not laughing at a joke is a response—sometimes emotional, sometimes cognitive but always a response.

We can't emphasize this point enough: We are talking about the differences between a personality trait and an emotional response.

- Personality traits are stable and difficult to change. They make up who we are at our core, how we see ourselves, and how others see us.
- Emotions are situational and fluid. Emotions are reflected in our reactions and responses to our environment, events, and people in the moment. They also influence how the rest of the world sees us.
- Just because both traits and emotions influence how the world sees us does not mean they are the same. They are very different because one is more malleable than the other.

Keep in mind that personality is something you are, not something you do. Emotional control is something you do, not something you are. We can change a behavior, but we cannot easily change a personality trait.

After a brain injury, it is our emotional control that changes, not our core personality. This is a critical distinction to make because we can work on emotional control. We can recognize, rework, and refine those reactions that are tied to our emotions.

And that is where the hope is found.

Communication's Role in Emotional Control

Communication and the whole communication loop is too expansive to be fully explored within these pages.

The important issue for you to understand and acknowledge, at this point, is that emotions are expressed and interpreted through both visible and invisible layers of communication. With each layer, there is an opportunity for understanding and misunderstanding.

Communication is a two-way street—a dance of interpretation and reading in meaning. It is not just you and your past experience communicating with the person in front of you—it is so much more. Each person acts and reacts, and after a brain injury those actions and reactions may not feel familiar to either party. Those changes in emotional expression add an unexpected layer to the whole communication process, making it stickier and riper for missteps.

When we try to mind-read—assume an intent based on what we think we know, see, and hear—we might unintentionally make a mistake. It is always okay to ask for clarification before assuming.

There are so many opportunities for miscommunication and misinterpretation in the whole communication process. Keep in mind that you *are* responsible for what you say and how you say it but you are also responsible for getting clarification—stopping and asking—when communication does not feel right.

- You *are* responsible for being aware that your words and actions *will be* interpreted.
- You are *not* responsible for *how* they are interpreted by others.
- You *are* responsible for understanding that your message—what you *thought* you were saying when it left your head—may not be received in exactly the same way.

Retraining and Regaining Emotional Control

Dealing with emotions and practicing skills that will help build

114

emotional control are critical steps to recovery and to navigating relationships. The following exercises are difficult, especially when living inside an all-encompassing brain injury.

Here is the key: Managing emotions sounds and feels like such a simple concept but it requires loads of control, a set of words to use, and an understanding of how those emotions show up.

How we express our emotions is multilayered and dynamic. Those layers include:

- how we respond or react,
- the words we use,
- body language, and
- tone of voice.

Patience, for all involved, is critical. Recovery can be a long journey and setbacks and plateaus are common. But, in the end, every step of that journey has its rewards.

Please keep in mind that the only way to get from frustration to peace is to try, practice, and then try again.

We now understand, and you may not yet, that these are not "one and done" exercises. Keep coming back to these exercises over and over and over and over. Again, the formula for understanding is peeling away the layers and getting in touch with:

- how we respond or react,
- the words we use,
- body language, and
- tone of voice.

Here is the really difficult part of doing these exercises: When dealing with human emotions, the variables change—it is like constantly trying to hit a bull's eye on a moving target.

There is a part of me that wants to scream "I am two years out! I should not feel this out of control. When am I going to be me again?" And I know that the way to move through is to keep working. I know it. But what if I fail? –Mary

And what if you don't?

What if you choose to redefine **failure** as *not* working at the things you know will make you better?

What if you choose to redefine **success** as understanding how you react and respond to all that is going on around you?

What if you choose to take the time to celebrate that understanding and then create an incentive for yourself to deepen that?

This is not easy work and these are not exercises that will *cure you* by magically turning you back into who you were pre-brain injury. They *will* help you find peace in knowing how, what, and where you might respond or react, and how that all fits within the parameters of your life right now.

You know what? You don't have to hit a bull's eye. The idea is to breathe a little more easily regardless of where you hit the target and be okay with it.

The truly crazy part, and the part we cannot overemphasize, is that how you feel and how you interact with the world will change as time passes. Your ability to control your emotions will vary, as will your patience. Keep coming back to these exercises. They will help you find your North and re-gain your balance.

It is never easy to work on emotional control—and you will probably think, "Oh I already did those exercises"—but keep working and make doing these exercises a *life practice*. The better you understand, the more automatic it all becomes and the easier it becomes to find that place of peace.

Exercise 10: Respond or React

This exercise is for both **S1 (survivor) and S2 (support)**.

The **goal** is simply to notice events without judgement.

At the end of the day, select three (3) things that you experienced that day and write one in each of the sections below. Record what happened in that specific situation.

Perhaps the dirty towels were left of the floor, the coffee overflowed, a butterfly flew next to you as you walked, your favorite food was on sale at the grocery store, a man at the corner spoke to you, or the dog jumped up on the bed.

Write down a few details describing the scene—no judgement, just the facts.

After you have recorded all the facts, take a minute and think about what you did in that moment. Did you respond or react? Circle RESPOND if you considered your next action, REACT if you gave your next move no thought, or NEITHER if you walked away, ignored, or detached.

Again, no judgement—there is no right answer here. You are simply choosing whether you thought through your response (RESPOND) or did you act without giving it much thought (REACT) or did you choose to do nothing (NEITHER).

List the events and record your reactions on the next pages.

EVENT #1

Circle one: **RESPOND**   **REACT**   **NEITHER**
Report the facts:

EVENT #2

Circle one: **RESPOND**   **REACT**   **NEITHER**
Report the facts:

EVENT #3

Circle one: **RESPOND**   **REACT**   **NEITHER**
Report the facts:

Wrap-up

As you might have found out through this exercise, the first step is to notice how you respond or react to a situation.

Remember, in this exercise, you were only noticing your responses and reactions, not judging, fixing or looking for causes.

Now take the next step and ask yourself the following eneral questions:

- Am I responding or reacting in a way that does not feel right?
  - Am I overreacting or under responding to situations?
  - Am I avoiding situations?
- Are others responding or reacting to me in a way that does not feel right?
  - Does it feel like others are avoiding me?
  - Do I feel misunderstood?

All too often, when you recognize changes in how you react to the world, especially ones that throw you for a loop and feel out of character, the most readily available responses are 1) denial and 2) defeat.

How can this be me and why can't I control my emotions?

What happened to the person that I was?

How can I regain any sense of who I am?

Will this change in me damage my relationships?

The purpose of this exercise was to recognize and acknowledge, without judgment, how you are reacting to the world and what those reactions might teach you.

This step might feel tedious, but it is essential. The information we get when we stop and notice provides the foundation upon which change is built.

Journal

Take a look at the workbook page you just completed, pick an item or two, and ask yourself these questions:

- *What, if any, changes in my reactions, have I noticed?*
- *Have those changes impacted life for me?*
- *How did I handle those changes?*
  - o *Did they knock me off balance or did I take them in stride?*
  - o *How quickly did I recover and move on?*

In the space below, write out a few of your thoughts.

_____

_____

_____

_____

_____

_____

_____

_____

_____

_____

EMOTIONAL VOCABULARY WORD BANK

The next step is to give a name to what is happening. Whether you like it or not, brain injuries take away bits and pieces of vocabulary—ways to express what is happening sometimes are just beyond reach.

No one really noticed that anything was wrong with me for a few days. Sure I was quiet and that was highly unusual. They figured I was sad or in pain or getting over losing my mid-life crisis car that I loved so much. No one understood that I just did not know how to tell them that everything was really wrong, scary wrong—I did not have the words nor the ability to search for them. –Ruth

That scenario, that loss of words and the immobilizing feeling that comes with the inability to find them, applies in so many circumstances post-brain injury. However, the situation where it is most exhausting is when you want to express your emotions. Talking about how you feel or understanding a reaction requires depth and color; it is this vocabulary that allows you to add detail to what is stirring inside and give it deeper meaning.

For example, you might notice the siren of a police car and, without much thought or feeling, take appropriate action by pulling the car over to the side of the road. However, the different tone of an ambulance siren might trigger a memory that causes every hair on your body to stand up, your stomach to churn, and a cold wave of fear to take hold.

Being able to verbally express the reactions to two seemingly similar sounds requires a completely different set of words to describe what is happening.

Because words have the unique ability to express what is going on inside, when your grip on language waivers, you may experience various emotions; these feelings *always* deserve recognition and respect.

The loss of words to adequately describe what you are feeling is one of the most destructive and divisive conditions post brain injury.

How can you expect anyone to understand, act, and react to you appropriately when you don't have the words to let them in?

Communication breakdowns can create a cycle of misunderstanding that goes beyond the situation at hand and can turn even benign circumstances into emotionally-charged, world-changing, relationship-altering meltdowns.

On pages 183 - 188 in the Appendix, you will find a list of words that convey emotion. Use these pages as cheat sheets while you refill your word bank with words that add the depth and color needed to express what you are experiencing and how you are feeling.

If you like, you can tear them out, fold them into smaller pieces, and carry them with you. Think of these sheets as your best tool to help you find the right word to express your feelings, big and small.

Exercise II: Describing the Scene

> This exercise is for **S1 (survivor)**.
>
> The **goal** is to practice using your emotional vocabulary in context.

Take out your emotional vocabulary word bank list (page 183). Examine the photos below. How does this scene make you feel? Using words from the list, both describe what is happening in the scene and how you are feeling.

Repeat this exercise, using the same picture, but choose different words to expand your vocabulary word bank.

Wrap-up

This exercise gave you an opportunity to practice using different words to describe how one scene made you feel. Once you rebuild your emotional vocabulary word bank, you will have the tools to express one feeling in multiple ways.

The more you practice, the more naturally words will come out. Repetition is your key to success.

Nonverbal Communication

Words are only one piece of communication. Nonverbal cues play a huge role in expanding the message, for both sender and receiver.

Body language—your physical expressions—helps to fill in emotions and intent that spoken words may have left out.

Let's take a closer look at some examples of body language and what they might indicate.

Body Language Cue	What That Cue Might Mean
Clenched Jaw	Stress, tension, focus, lack of sleep, anger, pain, resolve, determination, thoughtfulness
Slumped Shoulders	Defeat, depression, soreness/pain, resignation, relaxation, fatigue, lack of stress, boredom
Smile	Joy, nervousness, embarrassment, openness, friendliness, happiness, gas
Clenched Fists	Anger, frustration, control, determination, fear, anticipation
Leaning back	ease, confidence, disengagement, discomfort
Leaning forward	Attentiveness, anxiety, enthusiasm, avoidance, interest
Head tilted to one side	Curiosity, confusion, satisfied, agreement, bewilderment

Exercise 12: Reading Body Language

This exercise is for **S1 (Survivor)** and **S2 (Support)**

The **goal** is to notice nonverbal cues and how you interpret them.

Go to a public place such as a coffee shop/restaurant, library, the mall, a bus/train station, or park where you can sit comfortably and safely for at least 20 minutes. With this book and a pencil or pen, position yourself in spot where you can easily observe people passing by. As they pass, what gets your attention about their body language (see chart on previous page). Use the space below to record what body language cues you notice and what those cues might mean.

Person #1 **Body Language Cue**	**What That Cue Might Mean**

Let's do this again. With this book and a pencil or pen, position yourself in spot where you can easily and safely observe people passing by. As they pass, record below what gets your attention about their body language. Use the space below to record what body language cues you notice.

Person #2 **Body Language Cue**	**What That Cue Might Mean**

One more time, with this book and a pencil or pen, position yourself in spot where you can easily and safely observe people passing by. As they pass, record below what gets your attention about their body language. Use the space below to record what body language cues you notice.

Person #3 **Body Language Cue**	**What That Cue Might Mean**

Compare notes. What did each of you notice?

Wrap-up

When you scan someone you don't know, you are basically taking inventory of physical expressions. You are assessing how they might feel based on what you see, helping you to build a dictionary of emotional indicators.

As you work to understand body language, you begin to create a world outside of your head—one where you can see the world through someone else's eyes.

When you scan someone close to you, the situation becomes more personal and meaningful. You tend to interpret and fill in more gaps when you know someone and believe you can *tell* how they are feeling.

By including body language, you discover that there is another conversation going on beyond the words, a continual subtext. Pay attention to the cues and, when they don't seem to fit or make sense, *ask* for clarification.

The important thing to remember here is that even though body language can add to meaning, that meaning is often colored by other factors and is open for interpretation and misinterpretation.

Exercise 13: Self-tone

This exercise is for both **S1 (Survivor)** and **S2 (Support)**

The **goal** of this exercise is to help you understand how tone of voice can change the meaning of a message. Have fun with this one!

You will need a newspaper, book, or magazine and a voice recorder (phone, audio recorder, etc.). Pick a sentence from whatever reading material you chose. Your objective is to read that sentence in a variety of ways.

Turn on the recorder. The first time you read the sentence, imagine you are angry. Keep the recorder going. Pause for a few seconds and read that same sentence believing you are joyful. Read the sentence as if you were really feeling those emotions. Make an effort to insert tone as you read.

Keep the recording going, pause for a few seconds again and repeat the steps and read that same sentence as if you were:

- anxious
- calm
- in a hurry
- focused
- worried
- in control
- in pain
- celebrating a win

Play back your recording and listen carefully. Can you hear tone? Does tone change how you interpret the message?

Wrap-up

Reflecting on our last exercise, it becomes obvious that when you intentionally play with the inflection and volume of your voice, you hear different messages that underlie your words.

Here are the points to consider:

- The tone in your voice adds meaning to your words.

- That meaning can easily be misinterpreted by others.

Most of the time, we don't think about or consciously direct how our voice is heard by the rest of the world. We are more aware of *what* we are saying than *how* we are saying it.

Tone, the part of communication that you rarely consciously think about or direct, is one of the most used cues for others to figure out the emotions and intention behind your words. Tone of voice carries both intended and unintended meaning.

It is harder to find the right words now, so I am very deliberate when I speak—choosing my words carefully and speaking slowly so I get it right. I wish others knew that I am not angry or impatient, I am simply trying to get it right. – CA

When I am focused on a task and trying to make sure that my daughter understands what I want to accomplish, my voice comes out clipped and she, more often than not, interprets that as angry and short tempered. Honestly, I am just focused on getting from point A to point B. – JE

I woke up with a scorching headache. I had a meeting first thing and knew that it would take all my reserves to work around the pain. In that meeting, my voice came across as impatient, agitated, and frustrated, when what I really wanted to do was convey my point, not my pain! – CS

When you are operating at peak brain performance, the tone of your voice accurately mirrors how you feel. When you are in pain, struggling to block out distractions, trying to find the right words, or focusing on remembering all the details of a task, the tone in your voice carries so much more. Even though your tone reflects those hidden challenges, those you are speaking to will often personalize it, interpreting the inflection and modulation in your voice on a purely emotional level.

Exercise 14: Role Playing

This exercise is for **S1 (Survivor)** and **S2 (Support)**

The **goal** is to step outside your own experience and imagine how someone else might handle a situation.

Take a quick look at all the exercises you have done in this section before starting this exercise. Make sure that you have your vocabulary list next to you and have body language cues in mind because you will be using both here.

Begin this exercise by selecting a fictional character. This can be a character from a favorite TV show, book, or cartoon. It does not have to be a complicated character, the only really important factor is that you must feel like you know that character.

On small pieces of paper, write down the following scenarios: spilled a cup of coffee, running late for work, won a lottery prize, playing with a puppy, your friend gave you a cheeseburger, you smell smoke, a woman walked in smelling like roses, it is cloudy outside, it started to snow. Place individual scenarios into a bowl or hat.

Taking turns, select a scenario from the bowl/hat and act it out as you believe your selected character would behave. There is **no** right or wrong here, but there is lots of room to be silly, have fun, and experience the world from another's perspective.

A few things to avoid:

- Looking at the scenario as you would as *you*—the goal is to step outside your world and into someone else's.
- Over-analyzing both the situation (what is on the card) and the character and their motives—the point is to behave in the moment while thinking, in a playful way, like someone else.

A few things to focus on:

- Understand that there is no right or wrong here—it is just fun and this is an exercise to give you a break from living inside your own head.
- Just go with the scene as long as it feels good and you are having fun. If you feel you have completed the scene, stop and move to the next. Don't over-analyze. Escape into that fictional character's mind for a moment and imagine seeing the world through their eyes. Just go with it.

A few examples:

My character is Scooby Do and I picked running late for work.
"Rut ro, took me too long to find my Scooby Snacks...now I am in big trouble. Rye rope Shaggy is not mad at me. Mad Shaggy, no Scooby Snacks...rut ro, rut ro, rut ro…"

My character is Inspector Gamache (main character in Louise Penny's Three Pines mystery books) and I picked playing with a puppy.
"I wonder if the fact that she is playing with that puppy is a distraction? Is she hiding something or maybe just trying to calm herself? I have seen this behavior before and wonder if this situation is similar. I need to file that fact away for later."

Remember, you are stepping into that character's head in a specific moment in time. Get into the character but don't try to overplay it and don't try to extend it beyond that snapshot in time.

Wrap-up

The challenge of this exercise was to shift out of your own experience and see the world through someone else's eyes. This exercise both allowed you to consider someone else's perspective and to expand your own point of view, adding tools to your toolbox so that you have access to many paths of interpretation and action.

The idea is to recognize that others have feelings, habits, and ways to deal with the world that don't necessarily match yours. This fun activity demonstrates different ways of thinking about and seeing the world. In experiencing how that fictional character might react, you may also come up with some viable alternatives for the next time you run into a sticky situation. Options are a good thing.

Apathy, Empathy, and Moving Forward

I keep having this conversation with myself: Am I depressed? No, I don't think so. I second guess and question but realize that there are now things I don't care about anymore... but maybe I should. - Mary

Brain injury has a few odd, unexplained side effects. One of the strangest *and* most universal is apathy. Apathy – lack of interest, motivation, or emotion – can stem from a variety of conditions or states and is frequently mislabeled as depression or laziness.

- Medical practitioners will see depression.
- Friends and family might see a lack of motivation.
- Co-workers might see laziness.
- The world might think you don't care

.

> *It is not that I don't care. It is that I can't care. - Ruth*

What is important *here* is that almost *all* apathy triggers are closely tied to issues with emotional control and, in particular, the inability to see a world that exists outside your injured brain.

Honestly, there is no good research that goes beyond acknowledging apathy as a common condition after a brain injury. However, across the board, every single person with a brain injury that we have spoken to talks about periods of not being able to find meaning in life. They describe simply not caring. Although that may sound and feel to the outside world like depression or a plain unwillingness to try, it is—quite simply—apathy.

I had days when the fog in my brain felt so thick I just could not find anything that I cared about. My doctors thought I was depressed. My boss looked at me as if I was not trying very hard. I knew they were both wrong and also *knew in order to regain my balance I needed to get past what I knew was a major road block. I didn't have a name for it until much later, but how I dealt with my own apathy defined my path to recovery. In one of the rare moments when I did care, I made a conscious decision to **force** a **perspective** change and practice my formerly highly developed empathy skills. I created an exercise that made me pick a person and try tosee the world through their eyes. I started at home attempting to look at the world through my husband's and my son's eyes. I then worked my way out into the world, first with my mother and then to less safe, more foreign perspectives. This became part of my daily routine and led me deeper into my recovery than any other exercise in my repertoire. – Ruth*

It sounds odd, and maybe even unnatural, that practicing empathy can help you work your way out of the emotional fog that is so frequently part of brain injuries, but it can.

Bear in mind that this, like any other emotional control exercise, is not an instant fix or an easy process. You are working your way through a condition that is defined by a lack of action. This is hard work and a process you will need to repeat over and over and over before you see results.

Because apathy and empathy are both rooted in feeling, understanding how empathy can be used to work your way through apathy can be found in their definitions.

From the Merriam Webster Dictionary:

Apathy: *the feeling of not having much emotion or interest.*

Empathy: *the feeling that you **understand** and **share** another person's experiences and emotions; the ability to share someone else's feelings.*

The first step on this road is to "fake it until you make it." To do that, you will need to find a role model. In so many cases, that role model is just about anyone who is not wrapped up in the imperfections left behind by a brain injury. Move outside your head – your all-encompassing world – and see the world through their eyes.

Now, recognize that those around you have their own feelings. Yes, that sounds so basic, but that acknowledgement will help you move outside your thoughts, even for a second.

Next, try to understand the different ways of looking at, evaluating, and emotionally experiencing a situation. Take an issue—any thought or situation that can be looked at from multiple angles—and try to shift your perspective to look at it through a changed view.

Once that feels okay, from a safe distance watch how someone else reacts when presented with a problem and think about how their perspective feels.

Finally, next time you face a dilemma, stop yourself from responding and try to see the scenario through someone else's viewfinder.

The work you have done up to this point will help you see there are lives that are worse and lives that are better, but there are also lives not defined by a diagnosis. That provides a bit of light and, in some cases, the confidence and resolve to move forward.

Exercise 15: Empathy in Practice

> This exercise is for **S1 (Survivor)**
>
> The **goal** is to build and rebuild empathy.

This is an opportunity to observe, incorporate, and practice empathy.

In this exercise you will go deeper than just looking at the actions of another and take into consideration their feelings. First you will observe, then you will practice on your own. Here are the steps:

Step 1: Identify a role model. This is anyone who is able to move outside their own head and see the world through the eyes of another.

Step 2: Recognize your model has and is incorporating the ability to see the world through eyes outside their own head.

Step 3: Choose an event from your day – something that happened to you – where you had to interact with someone else.

Step 4: Replay that scene in your head but look at it through your role model's perspective.

Step 5: Repeat this exercise at least once a week until it feels natural to see the world through someone else's eyes.

Wrap-up

The practice of shifting perspective and pushing beyond what you see in your head can absolutely heighten your healing.

As you might have found in the previous exercise, practicing empathy helps you find meaning, and although not yet proven, could also help build a better brain. Think about these two big benefits:

- First, practicing *empathy* serves as a distraction and can keep you from falling down the rabbit hole that turns apathy into despair. It can move you to a place bigger than yourself, open up the world to look beyond injury or disease progression, and live in this moment.
- Second, seeing the world through someone else's eyes provides a glimpse at the depth of human perspective and begins rewiring your brain. We know that changing your view makes you *feel,* which, in turn, fires up activity in your brain.

It's those "A-ha" moments, the moments when you realize the power of experiencing other points of view, that set a sustainable path towards actively engaging in the world outside your head. Putting yourself in others' shoes helps you shift from that exclusively internal dialogue to acknowledging the other side of the issue. This shift in your focus allows you to step outside of your head so that you can move towards compassion and connection.

Imagine this scenario. You just dropped your daughter off at the bus station and a man runs out from between cars, right in front of your car. You might be thinking:

- Didn't your mother ever teach you not to run out from between cars?
- Don't stare at me Buddy, you are the one who ran out in front of me.
- You should be grateful I didn't just hit you.

Now take a deep breath and consider his thoughts:

- Oh no, I'm going to miss my bus.
- If I am late for work one more time, I might lose my job.
- I can't be late for this meeting…. They are counting on me.
- Oh no…. there's a car coming at me.
- What the heck is wrong with her? She almost ran me over!

Once you make that shift and put yourself in someone else's shoes, you can begin to move past the confines of your own thoughts and emotions, regaining a perspective that will help you move forward with enhanced empathy.

Journal

There are many opportunities to practice empathy. Pick an event from your day and imagine the whole scenario from the other side. How does it feel to put yourself in someone else's emotional world? Does it shift how you want to act or react to the situation? If it does, how does that make you feel? Write out your thoughts in the space below.

CHAPTER THIRTEEN
Bridge to the Fourth Corner

Vision is at the ultimate intersection between all the side-effects of brain injury—it mingles with changes in attention and cognitive functioning that result in changes in emotional control. It is the one place where you can literally **see** a brain injury—where symptoms manifest in tangible ways that allow us a window inside the changed brain.

That overlap is obvious in a few very basic activities you do every day; in particular, your ability to read and your ability to drive. These are both multi-layered activities and involve so much more than being able to see or focus your eyes. They incorporate cognitive functions and attentional issues and even emotional control issues. In these two cases, separating out vision is not a realistic or helpful approach because that ignores everything else that is going on.

First, vision is foundational to how we understand the world around us. We use vision as our primary filter—more than 70% of the information we take in is through sight. When *how you see* changes, and you view the world through a distorted lens, life changes dramatically.

You can think about vision as located at the junction of so

many brain functions. It helps you keep your balance; it moves you from a flat picture to a 3-D world; it enhances all the other senses by completing the picture; it allows you, literally, to focus on what is in front of you, behind you, and beyond you. Vision keeps you from running into both literal and figurative obstacles.

Second, we are talking about changes in vision post brain injury because, frankly, many others are not. Looking for changes in vision, beyond asking if there is blurred vision, is not typically part of standard post brain injury assessment protocols. However, vision changes may appear in the days, weeks, and months following a brain injury. That is why we believe this discussion is critical.

It is quite possible that increased awareness, early intervention, and improved follow up with vision issues can elevate the course of recovery from brain injury.

Third, problems with vision are often swallowed up by the other changes that we have discussed, namely cognitive rewiring, attention shifts, and emotional challenges. The overlap is extreme and the shared root of the difficulty is often not addressed.

Identifying disconnects in the brain-eye connection and how you process visual information may be a central, and often overlooked, missing link in evaluation and treatment protocols.

Vision is assessed through mechanics, often through the examination of changes in eye shape, optic nerve functionality and eye movement. Focusing solely on mechanical changes makes it easy to overlook the results of misfires in processing due to brain injury.

*Nobody told me that depth perception and balance were things I could lose…. My shins were bruised and bleeding from running into things, and my hands, elbows, and knees were full of scrapes from falling. I couldn't judge where anything was. I didn't know the coffee table—the one that had been in the same spot in my living room for ten years —was right in front of me until my shin slammed into it. Nor could I judge where the last stair was until I stepped for the landing only to find I was already there. No balance. No depth perception. No sense of direction. Why doesn't anybody talk about **those** side effects? Sure would have made figuring out how to fix it all that much easier.   - Ruth*

Journal

Think about where you may be experiencing challenges that haven't been named or don't seem to fit in the category that they were assigned. You know they are real–they just need a name…. Do you feel there is something that is being missed or is still unnamed? Record those thoughts below.

CHAPTER FOURTEEN
Changes in Vision

As discussed in the previous section, changes in visual processing are tricky because they are often easily explained away as changes in cognitive, attentional, or emotional function. Vision changes are often very subtle and get lost in the assessment process.

The impact of misfires in visual processing is so much bigger than any simple eye test can reveal or predict. How your brain takes in visual information and makes sense out of it dictates how you *see* and live in the world. Your reliance on the accuracy of that picture cannot be overstated—*you literally need what you see to be accurate to survive and thrive.*

This whole concept is immense and one that is not easy to grasp. As you know, your brain gets bits and pieces of information from everything that is going on around you and it takes that information and routes it for processing. You also know that brain injuries often result in closed pathways and when information gets sent down a nonfunctioning pathway, normal processing misfires. When that happens with visual information, the result can be enormous.

I had to walk in a circular path around my wife and make subtle gestures so that she would see me gradually come up on her and not get startled. I knew that she was missing a chunk of her visual field and simply could not see me until I was right there next to her. –DC

I did not want to offend her or make her feel as though she could not take care of herself but I saw that hairbrush that she had been searching for, sitting on the counter, right in front of her but right in the center of her blind spot. –AC

Consider this: If you can't see what is not visible to you and you don't know it is missing...you just don't know what you don't know.

Visual changes post brain injury can manifest in a variety of ways. In this section, however, we will look at three relatively common conditions associated with changes in visual processing: missing visual field, loss of depth perception, and lack of convergence (the eyes' ability to work together to focus and track).

When you are missing a part of your ***visual field***, bits and pieces, and sometimes even chunks, of the entire picture just don't exist for you. You routinely miss everything that exists in the areas that you simply can't see. For example, you are not able to see the hairbrush on the counter because it is not in your functioning field of vision. You can't see the dog at your feet when he is positioned within your "blind spot". Again, you don't know what you don't know and you can't acknowledge what you don't see.

When you lose your ***depth perception,*** it is nearly impossible to judge where you are in space relative to the rest of the world. You could run into the table that hasn't moved in five years or miss the cup when pouring coffee. You might not be able to judge how far you are from the wall or how far you must reach to pick up the TV remote.

When your eyes are not working together *(convergence)*, images jump, change form, and disappear. For example, words on the page blur, turn to dots or seem to float off, out of your awareness. Or you might miss the object that is coming at you or only maintain focus on an image with one eye closed.

To further complicate this whole picture, changes in visual processing don't always show up during initial assessments post brain injury. Often there is a series of events triggered by a pathway shut-down within the brain that can lead to additional shut downs, resulting in a series of process malfunctions. For example, you may not have had double vision immediately after your initial brain injury or at the time of your initial assessment. That does not mean that double vision will not pop-up in the days, weeks, or months to come.

Changes in vision can creep in later and can, literally and figuratively, throw you off balance. Pay attention, not just in the initial days following a brain injury, but in the long run for changes in vision. Following up and following through with vision training when changes are noticed is critical to healing and recovery.

Strengthening the Brain-Eye Connection

One of the best ways to strengthen the brain-eye connection is to work on those skills that force your eyes to work together while actively filtering out extraneous information.

Before starting the following exercises, it is extremely important to remember not to push yourself beyond fatigue for several reasons.

First, working your eyes taxes your brain. There are few tasks that will deplete cognitive reserve quicker than overworking your eyes. Eye strain and exhaustion often go hand in hand!

Second, exercises that force your eyes to work together not only work the brain-eye connection but they also work the muscles that control the movement of your eyes. Those muscles fatigue with overuse.

Be mindful and don't overwork your eyes!

Exercise 16: Visual Tracking

This exercise is for **S1 (Survivor)** and **S2 (Support)**

The **goal** is to strengthen the brain-eye connection by training the eyes to work together more effectively.

For this exercise you will need a hollow ball like a tennis or racquetball, a piece of twine or strong fishing line, and something like a pair of scissors or sharp knife to poke a hole through the ball. Take your sharp object and make a hole all the way through the ball. The hole needs to only be big enough to fit your piece of twine or fishing line through. Thread the piece of twine through the hole and tie a knot on both ends that prevents the string from passing through the hole.

Start with S1 sitting in a chair. S2 stands about 15 feet in front of S1 holding the string with the ball hanging down. S2 swings the ball so it is moving from side to side, slowly. S1 focuses on the ball as it swings. Stop after about 10 side-to-side cycles or when it becomes difficult to focus. At the end of this cycle, S1 closes their eyes and counts to 20.

Next, S2 takes a step toward S1, cutting the distance by about ⅓. S1 opens their eyes. Again, S2 swings the ball slowly side to side and S1 focuses for about 10 cycles or until it uncomfortable. Once more, S1 closes their eyes and counts to 20.

Finally, S2 takes one more step forward (standing about 5 feet in front of S1) and repeats this exercise.

Discuss your observations. Did you notice any changes in posture, head movement, facial expressions, or eye movement as the cycles repeated? Was there a focal length that seemed more comfortable? How might you incorporate this information in your role as a partner in healing?

Wrap-up

It is not uncommon to be able to tell that you worked your eyes hard at the end of this type of exercise. Most of the time, your eyes work much like a camera set on autofocus, automatically adjusting for different focal point conditions. In this exercise, you took your eyes off autofocus and set them to manual. You gave them shifting focal points, requiring your eyes and brain to work harder.

You might also have noticed how *quickly* your eyes fatigued and how much that eye fatigue tires your brain—especially when you force your eyes to focus intensely and work together.

Vision is such an automatic process that when you push yourself to use your eyes differently, even when compensating for a change that is related to a brain injury, you are overriding years of autofocus training and will invariably encounter resistance.

Keep practicing and your eyes—both muscles and brain connections—will get used to the new twist on an old task.

Exercise 17: Brain-Eye Tracking

This exercise is for **S1 (Survivor)** and **S2 (Support)**

The **goal** is to strengthen the brain-eye connection by training the eyes to work together.

In this extremely simple series of exercises you will need two ping-pong balls and a flat surface.

In step one, **S1** holds the ping-pong ball at eye level and drops it on the flat surface then catches the ball as it bounces back up. Repeat this 10 times. Do not move to the next step until **S1** has mastered this.

Next, **S1** and **S2** sit across from each other at a table, starting with **S2** holding a ping-pong ball at eye level. **S1** focuses on the ball. On the count of three, **S2** bounces the ball across the table to **S1**. The objective is to focus on the bouncing ball and track it all the way to the hand. **S1** catches the ball and then bounces the ball back to **S2.** Repeat until you are no longer having fun.

This optional step provides additional challenge and should only be attempted once you have mastered the above activities. Once again, sit across from each other but this time each of you (**S1** and **S2)** has a ball. Each holds their ball at eye level and bounces their ball, at the same time across the table to the other. Your goal is to track the ball as it leaves your partner's hand and follow it all the way to your hand. The *challenge* is to shift your focus from your ball, the one that just left your hand, to the ball that is coming at you. This is much harder than it sounds. Be patient.

Wrap-up

These exercises might help you realize that vision is not a passive activity. Because processing visual information feels automatic, the complexity and importance of the brain-eye connection is often underestimated and underappreciated.

When you focus on exercises to strengthen the brain-eye connection, you recognize the cognitive efforts behind that process and the importance of it working well.

The Importance of the Brain-Eye Connection

Consider this:

- In **every** given moment, your brain is assigning meaning to *every* single detail, *every* aspect, of *everything* your eyes **see**.

Now, think about this:

- This process **never** shuts down.

Post brain injury, visual processing fatigues very quickly primarily because there is no off switch—awake or asleep, the brain-eye connection is *always* working.

When working to strengthen the brain-eye connection, keep in mind that you can actually use up all of your cognitive and physical reserves just through visual processing. The brain-eye connection is critical to helping you understand the world but also requires lots of energy.

It is often more difficult to recover from the muscle fatigue that happens when your eyes are working than the cognitive fatigue. Both require rest but the only way to rest those eye muscles is to not use them at all. That is not possible.

Most of the time when you think about resting a muscle group, you consider things like sitting and reading, watching TV, or sleeping. These so-called resting activities can actually work eye muscles even harder. For example, reading requires you to focus on a page, a TV has a screen with changing light, and you experience rapid eye movements during sleep.

When fatigue hits, consider finding a blank space on a wall and resting your gaze. Recovery will happen naturally as long as you don't continue to overtax the process.

The brain-eye connection always needs work, regardless of stage of life and health status. Improving how well your brain and your eyes work together will help you process visual information more effectively and efficiently in a less taxing manner. The better your brain-eye connection, the lower the burden on your cognitive and physical reserves.

Exercise 18: Rebuilding Depth Perception

> This exercise is for **S1 (Survivor)**
>
> The **goal** is to ease difficulties judging where you are in relation to objects around you.

In this exercise, you will, literally, put one foot in front of the other.

Set aside at least one time slot (15 to 30 minutes) each day when you are not rushed. Make sure you have this workbook and a pencil.

Pick 5 different starting points. On the chart below, write those starting points down in the column labeled Starting Point. These could be "Standing inside the front door" or "Standing at the flagpole at the park" or "Standing in front of stove".

Now pick a logical, relatively close, ending point and write that in the Ending Point column. That ending point might be "the coffee table" or "the first tree on the left" or "the kitchen table".

In the beginning, pick points that are within your line of sight and are without obstacles (stairs, doors, furniture, trees, streets, etc.) that will hinder you. It is important to keep it simple.

Stand at the starting point and put one foot directly in front of the other as you would if you were walking a line.

Counting the number of your steps, continue to move forward, putting one foot in front of the other, until you get to the ending point.

Write down the number of steps you took in the Steps column.

Each session should always have 5 different starting points.

Starting Point	Ending Point	# of Steps

CHANGES IN VISION

Starting Point	Ending Point	# of Steps

Starting Point	Ending Point	# of Steps

Starting Point	Ending Point	# of Steps

Wrap-up

As you continue to work through this exercise, you are building a library filled with reference points that help you judge where you are in time and space—one you can use for future reference to navigate the world safely and confidently.

Sometimes, after a brain injury, that ability to judge distance, for whatever reason, fails. The more you focus on measuring distance, the easier and more automatic it becomes and the more extensive your library of references points.

Journal

What did you learn about vision changes? How do those changes relate to you? Do those changes impact your day-to-day life? Share your thoughts in the space below.

_____

_____

_____

_____

_____

_____

_____

_____

_____

_____

_____

_____

_____

_____

_____

_____

_____

CHAPTER FIFTEEN
The Book Club

Just as we have bridged the four corners, Book Club is rooted in working together and connects all the exercises in this book.

Book Club is so much bigger than any single exercise. It is comprehensive and incorporates aspects of the four corners of brain functioning that we have discussed. It is a flexible, ongoing activity designed to be enjoyable and always brings benefit, no matter the level of functioning or how many times you repeat it.

Unlike any other activity in this book, there is no real wrap-up to Book Club because this is a continuing activity. Each time you repeat it, you will grow, sometimes in different ways. We suggest that you take some time at the end of each book and look at:

- How you grew, both individually and together as a team.
- How your learnings were different in this book from the last.
- What challenged you and how can you use that challenge to move forward on your path.

175

The Book Club

> Book Club is an incredibly powerful exercise for **S1 (Survivor)** and **S2 (Support)**.
>
> The **goal** is to maintain Book Club over the long-term and, in the process, rebuild emotional connection and control, spark imagination, provide a valuable escape, and deepen empathy.

The ultimate goal of this exercise is to be able to see the world through the eyes of a few of the characters in each selected book. In order to do that, you will need to dive into that character's personality and ways of dealing with the world. In the beginning you will look at many characters. Then, you will narrow that list to a few characters that you will get to know better with each reading. Take this step by step.

Step 1: Pick a book that strikes your interest.

The best books to use for this exercise are those with well-developed characters. Detective and legal novels work very well. Authors like Louise Penny, Henning Mankell, Jussi Adler-Olsen, R.D. Wingfield, Michael Connelly, Tana French, and John Grisham do a wonderful job of creating rich characters that work beautifully for this exercise. Other types of stories can work and popular authors like JoJo Moyes and Liane Moriarty also paint beautiful, distinctly identifiable characters.

Two big cautions to keep this exercise zeroed in on understanding how others interact with the world:
1. Make sure that there are not too many plot lines. The characters need to be the focus of the book.
2. Avoid books that are heavy on symbolism and use veiled or complicated language. Again, the focus, for

176

the purpose of this exercise, is to dive into the characters. Because of their complexity, it is a good idea to avoid the "classics" and most nonfiction.

Step 2: Set aside *at least* one, 60 to 90 minute period each week for this exercise. Even though reading a novel feels like a luxury activity, Book Club is therapy and it is critical to make time to do this exercise consistently to take your healing to another level.

Step 3: Start reading out loud to each other. If the survivor is having difficulty reading out loud, for any reason, limit their activity to questions and answers about the characters and to ensure that they are following along. Make small steps to get both involved in the reading out loud but slowly and gently. This exercise works best if it is enjoyable. Struggling to follow the words as they dance across the page or making your eyes focus when they don't want to cooperate is not enjoyable.

Step 4: Use a Character Sheet (sample on page 197) to list the characters as it becomes apparent they are important – one character per sheet – and list details about what that character is like. Leave 20 to 30 minutes at the end of each session to record, review, process, and add some details – again, make sure this is collaborative process – a conversation where both survivor and support are contributing.

Before filling in details about characters, make sure that all characters that feel important have their own sheet. You might initially glance over a character and not record them in the moment because they did not seem all that important at the time.

Next, use the areas on the Character Sheets to list what you learned about that character in the section you just read. As indicated on the sheet and shown in the example, circle either *personality trait* or *emotion* next to each descriptor.

Step 5: At the beginning of the next session, take a few minutes to review the characters. Have a brief conversation about whether you know enough about each to get a sense of who they are. This may feel awkward at first and not make much sense, however, it will get easier as you practice this skill.

REPEAT THE ABOVE FOR THREE SESSIONS. After three sessions move to Step 6.

Step 6: At the beginning of the fourth session, spread out all the Getting to Know the Character Sheets and separate them into two piles: one that has more than three items listed and one for sheets that have fewer than three items. Decide which characters you feel you know better based on the items listed on the sheet. Set aside the sheets for those that you either are not sure if they are important characters yet or if you feel they are not important characters. You can always put them back in the mix.

Read out loud as before. As always, with your last 20-30 minutes, take out your important Character Sheets. Add anything new you learned about each important character during that day's reading. Use the rest of the time at the end of the session to move to Step 7.

Step 7: Take out a Character Map Sheet and start to fill in the branches. Build as accurate a picture as possible for each important character.

Step 8: Each of the next sessions until you finish the book choose **one** of the following exercises:

- S2 picks a passage that they readily associate with one of the important characters in the book and reads it aloud to S1. S1 then identifies which character that passage was referring to or who said it.

- Take your favorite character and do the Role Playing exercise (see pages 139 and 140).

This exercise was built to be repeated and gets better and more enjoyable with each book. It is really important to follow the steps, one by one, every time you start this exercise with a new book.

Some find it helpful to read books by a brain injury or stroke survivor/caregiver. Reading about others' journeys will help you understand that 1) you are not alone and 2) that someone else made it out of the fog and wrote about it. Pick this book carefully – make sure the focus is on recovery and, like above, you can get to know how the characters in the book feel, act, and react. Here are some favorites to choose from:

Being Brain Healthy
I'll Carry the Fork
Stroke of Insight
Where is the Mango Princess
Stir

CHAPTER SIXTEEN
A Look Back

Hindsight, as they say, is 20-20.

Setting out on this project, we knew that we were embarking on something big. Somewhere along the journey we realized it was far bigger than either of our, or any other one individual's journeys. We realized there is a collective thread that connects all survivors of brain injury and weaves us into a shared fabric.

The first things we discovered were things that came from our conversations with others. We recognized the importance of healing as a shared, but still individual, journey. That made us dig deeper and reevaluate what we were doing and, perhaps more importantly, why we were doing it.

Our first exercise, the one where we challenged ourselves to notice everything, began to reveal the first part of "the why". It brought an awareness that neither of us expected. Our purpose moved beyond merely providing tips, tricks, and ways to compensate post-brain injury. We realized this book needed to be active. It needed to be a workbook.

As we crafted the first set of exercises, we realized the value of shared experiences. Those shared experiences help us build a stronger, more multidimensional partnership—one that will better stand up to the trials of healing. That was the "A-ha" moment that these exercises were not solely for our good, but benefit our support.

We knew, at that moment, that we needed to give voice to both sides of the equation.

By creating a workbook filled with activities for both survivor and their support, we moved beyond "Do you need a cup of tea?" and "Did you take your medicine?" to shared experiences that bring healing, understanding, and compassion to both.

Armed with a deeper understanding of our "why", we dug in.

As we dug, we found:

I underestimated the value of laughter and joy in my recovery and in my life. Mary

I overestimated how much I had healed. Ruth

I did not realize how vulnerable I really was until we started unpacking emotional control. Mary

I did not understand how bitter I still am about the visual processing deficits that I knew were real but no one acknowledged and are still denying. Ruth

I was unaware that the pain and the fear we unearthed in the digging process would be so intense. Mary

I had no idea how heart wrenching it would be to watch intense healing that closely. It was so profoundly different to experience the pain and agony of Mary's healing rather than my own. We lived this process together and walked it, step by step, together—Mary for the first time and me… reliving the struggle. Ruth

The process of writing this book opened a dialogue with my family. I allowed them, for the first time, to openly share how they feel about my new normal, the way I am today. That helped to express their fears and heal as well. I grossly underestimated the impact on my family. Mary

I realized that ripples of my words, my stories, and my experience reach beyond what even I can imagine. Ruth

I discovered that my brain injury was not just mine— everyone around was hurt as well. Through this process we started to heal together and rebuild, stronger together. Mary

The healing doesn't stop. I am so many years out and I still fake it every single day. Ruth

When I gave it a name, brain injury stopped having power over me. Mary

In trying to re-capture who we once were, we overestimate who we once were and set that bar entirely too high. I was never as good at mutli-tasking or remembering as I tried to tell myself. Ruth

When I began openly talking to friends about my brain injury, I stopped feeling shamed and flawed. Mary

It's about continually searching for that balance between recovery and denial, every single day... Ruth

Healing is richer and more effective when it is an open and shared experience. Mary & Ruth

There is no finish-line or due date in the healing process. Mary & Ruth

Throughout the healing process remember to:

- Breathe
- Laugh
- And, share the moments.

Appendix

Emotional Vocabulary List

Understanding	Confident	Reliable
Easy	Amazed	Free
Sympathetic	Interested	Satisfied
Receptive	Accepting	Kind
Happy	Great	Gay
Joyous	Lucky	Fortunate
Delighted	Overjoyed	Gleeful
Thankful	Important	Festive
Ecstatic	Satisfied	Glad
Cheerful	Sunny	Merry
Elated	Jubilant	Alive
Playful	Courageous	Energetic
Liberated	Optimistic	Provocative
Impulsive	Free	Frisky
Animated	Spirited	Thrilled
Wonderful	Good	Calm
Peaceful	At ease	Comfortable
Pleased	Encouraged	Clever
Concerned	Affected	Fascinated
Intrigued	Absorbed	Inquisitive
Nosy	Snoopy	Engrossed
Curious	Surprised	Content

Quiet	Certain	Relaxed
Serene	Free and easy	Bright
Blessed	Reassured	Loving
Considerate	Affectionate	Sensitive
Tender	Devoted	Attracted
Passionate	Admiration	Warm
Touched	Sympathy	Close
Loved	Comforted	Eager
Keen	Earnest	Intent
Anxious	Inspired	Determined
Excited	Enthusiastic	Bold
Brave	Daring	Challenged
Optimistic	Re-enforced	Confident
Hopeful	Strong	Positive
Interested	Impulsive	Free
Sure	Certain	Rebellious
Unique	Dynamic	Tenacious
Hardy	Secure	Angry
Irritated	Enraged	Hostile
Insulting	Sore	Annoyed
Upset	Hateful	Unpleasant
Offensive	Bitter	Aggressive
Resentful	Inflamed	Provoked
Incensed	Infuriated	Cross
Worked up	Boiling	Fuming

Indignant	Indifferent	Insensitive
Dull	Nonchalant	Neutral
Reserved	Weary	Bored
Preoccupied	Cold	Disinterested
Lifeless	Depressed	Lousy
Disappointed	Discouraged	Ashamed
Powerless	Diminished	Guilty
Dissatisfied	Miserable	Detestable
Repugnant	Despicable	Disgusting
Abominable	Terrible	In despair
Sulky	Bad	
A sense of loss	Afraid	Fearful
Terrified	Suspicious	Anxious
Alarmed	Panic	Nervous
Scared	Worried	Frightened
Timid	Shaky	Restless
Doubtful	Threatened	Cowardly
Quaking	Menaced	Wary
Confused	Upset	Doubtful
Uncertain	Indecisive	Perplexed
Embarrassed	Hesitant	Shy
Stupefied	Disillusioned	Unbelieving
Skeptical	Distrustful	Misgiving
Lost	Unsure	Uneasy
Pessimistic	Tense	Hurt

Crushed	Tormented	Deprived
Pained	Tortured	Dejected
Rejected	Injured	Offended
Afflicted	Aching	Victimized
Heartbroken	Agonized	Helpless
Incapable	Alone	Paralyzed
Fatigued	Useless	Inferior
Vulnerable	Empty	Forced
Hesitant	Despair	Frustrated
Distressed	Woeful	Pathetic
Tragic	In a stew	Dominated
Sad	Tearful	Sorrowful
Pained	Grief	Anguish
Desolate	Desperate	Pessimistic
Unhappy	Lonely	Grieved
Mournful	Dismayed	Threatened
Cowardly	Quaking	Alienated
Wary	Appalled	Humiliated

RECOGNIZING THE SIGNS WORKSHEET

Details of the situation #1:

What happened when you started to feel overwhelm?

Details of the situation #2:

What happened when you started to feel overwhelm?

RECOGNIZING THE SIGNS WORKSHEET

Details of the situation #1:

What happened when you started to feel overwhelm?

Details of the situation #2:

What happened when you started to feel overwhelm?

RECOGNIZING THE SIGNS WORKSHEET

Details of the situation #1:

What happened when you started to feel overwhelm?

Details of the situation #2:

What happened when you started to feel overwhelm?

RECOGNIZING THE SIGNS WORKSHEET

Details of the situation #1:

What happened when you started to feel overwhelm?

Details of the situation #2:

What happened when you started to feel overwhelm?

RECOGNIZING THE SIGNS WORKSHEET

Details of the situation #1:

What happened when you started to feel overwhelm?

Details of the situation #2:

What happened when you started to feel overwhelm?

Solutions to Exercise 8

Make a hard boiled egg
1. Get out a pan large enough to boil eggs.
2. Place the pan in the sink.
3. Get the carton of eggs from the refrigerator.
4. Place the carton on the counter.
5. Open the egg carton and carefully place the desired number of eggs in the pan.
6. Put just enough water in the pan to completely cover the eggs.
7. Place the pan on the stove.
8. Turn the burner on high.
9. Bring the water to a boil.
10. Turn off the burner.
11. Cover the pan with a lid.
12. Let the eggs stand for roughly 12 minutes.
13. Drain the water immediately and run cold water over the eggs.
14. When the eggs are cool, remove them from the pan.
15. Store the eggs in the refrigerator.
16. Clean the pan and put away any remaining eggs and supplies.

Pay a bill by mail
1. Take the envelope from the mailbox or, if you get your bill through an email, open the link to your bill.
2. Gather all supplies you will need to complete the process: checkbook, pen, envelope, and stamp.
3. If you received the bill in the mail, open the envelope and pull out the bill.
4. If there is a return envelope, set it aside.
5. If you received the bill electronically, print it.
6. Look at the bill and find the amount due.
7. Open the checkbook and write out the check for the amount due.
8. Double check to make sure you filled in the date, who it is to, the amount (both in numbers and words), the account number (if appropriate), and signed it.
9. Tear off the return portion needed to accompany your payment and fill in the amount paid.

10. Place both your check and the payment stub into the return envelope if one was included.
11. If the bill came electronically or if there was no return envelope, locate the address on the bill and write it on the envelope.
12. Place both your check and payment stub in the envelope.
13. Seal the envelope.
14. Place a stamp on your envelope and write your return address in the upper left corner.
15. Place the envelope in the mailbox.

Make a Peanut butter & jelly sandwich

1. Pull out a bag of bread and a jar of peanut butter and a jar of jelly.
2. Get out a dinner knife.
3. Open the bread and take out two slices.
4. Reclose the bread bag and set aside.
5. Open the peanut butter and, using your knife, scoop out large dollop.
6. Place the dollop on one slice of bread.
7. Spread the peanut butter evenly on that one slice.
8. Wipe any residual peanut butter on the other slice of bread to clean your knife.
9. Reclose the peanut butter.
10. Open the jelly and, using your knife, scoop out a large dollop.
11. Place the dollop on the slice of bread you used to clean off the residual peanut butter.
12. Spread the jelly evenly on that slice of bread.
13. Close the jelly.
14. Place the slices of bread together.
15. Place your sandwich on a plate.
16. Put away your supplies and wipe up the crumbs left on the counter.
17. Enjoy your sandwich!

Set an appointment with the doctor

1. Locate the doctor's phone number.
2. Have your calendar or planner near you and ready.
3. If it is a paper calendar, make sure you have a working pen or pencil ready.

4. Make sure you have your insurance card or any other paperwork the doctor's office will need, available and ready to use.
5. Pick up the phone and dial the doctor's phone number.
6. Explain to the receptionist you'd like to set an appointment and the purpose for your visit.
7. Enter the appointment into your planner or calendar.
8. Ask the receptionist what you need to bring with you.
9. Record any additional information in your calendar (this works both on a phone/electronic calendar or an appointment book/planner).
10. Confirm all the information including date, time, and what you need to bring with you, with the receptionist.
11. End the call.

Additional tasks:
- Replant a houseplant
- Feed a dog or cat
- Fold a pair of pants
- Brush your teeth
- Tie a shoe

CHARACTER SHEET

This is a sample. You can make your own or print them at
www.insidersguidetotheinjuredbrain.com/exercises.
Your access code is *thankyou*

Character Name:_____

What is this person like? List personality traits below:

Acknowledgements

From Mary:

To my husband, John, and my daughters, Caitlin and Alexis, I am so very thankful for each of you. Your endless love, honesty, patience, and understanding anchor me in hope and have helped us forge a true partnership in healing. You are my foundation and the very heart of my being. A huge, heartfelt thank you to Ruth Curran, my co-author and dear friend; it's been a long, fabulous, laughter-filled journey of discovery and healing. Words cannot express the depths of my gratitude to *and* for you. We have shared countless early mornings, 1 brain, 4 arms, lots of coffee, and lots pencil finding, and your bright light has made this wild ride worth every moment. And to your husband, Dan Curran, my thanks for your listening ears, gracious feedback, peaceful spirit, and pre-dawn humor. Finally, deep gratitude to the many survivors and their support who shared their stories of healing and hope with me. Your stories inspire me to do more, share more, and be more every day.

From Ruth:

First and foremost, a huge, never ending thanks to my co-author, treasured friend, and partner in laughter, Mary. Thank you, Mary, for pushing through the rough spots, working through the tough spots, and laughing through this amazing process with me. Thanks also to Tracy Teregis who introduced me to the idea and value of reading with survivors. I am so grateful that you brought your version of BooKlub into my world and helped me through the initial phases of taking the idea in a whole different direction. A special and incredibly warm thanks to all of those who spoke to me and told me their stories. This book and hopefully some lives, are better because of all of you. I am also eternally grateful to David for reminding, by your consistent actions, just how valuable unwavering patience, understanding, support, and the perfect amount of humor from adult children can be. That and you are irreplaceable. And… thanks to Dan for putting up with Mary's and my ***very*** early morning work sessions and for joining in on our laughter and tears as we worked through the writing of this book. You are, without question, the other half of my soul.

From both of us:

Thanks to our amazing editor, Sara Mark. You made our voices sing in harmony and we are grateful. We are also grateful to Caitlin Lanzavecchia, our production coordinator. Your eye for detail and beautiful perspective helped us more than you can possibly imagine.

A special thank you to our partner in crime and treasured friend, Lois. Your advice and your encouragement pushed us over the hurdles and we are so grateful.

You will find copies of all workbook pages on a secret page on www.insidersguidetotheinjuredbrain.com. Click on the button that says EXERCISES on the Home page. The secret password, the one you get by reading this, is *openplease*.

ABOUT THE AUTHORS

Brain injury survivor Mary Lanzavecchia writes from personal experience navigating life from inside an injured brain. In December 2015, a car accident left her engulfed, once again, in the fog of a brain injury – a place she has been at least five times since her teens. Always determined to move forward with optimism, Mary uses her experience, her writing, and her creative passions to work through the challenges of living with a brain injury.

After spending 17 years homeschooling her two daughters, Mary raises puppies for Guide Dogs for the Blind, teaches critical thinking to high school home schoolers, and writes and speaks about thriving your way through life's challenges, transitions, and renewals. Find her writing both on www.reclaimingmary.com and www.insidersguidetotheinjuredbrain.com.

Ruth Curran is passionate about the connection between the brain and daily functioning and believes everyone—regardless of age or stage of life—has the ability to use neuroplasticity to live a richer, deeper, more fully engaged life. Drawing on her experience successfully overcoming a traumatic brain injury sustained in an automobile accident, Ruth Curran, MS is an expert on maximizing brain health and function through lifestyle modification and "turning up the noise on life." She has created a series of photo-based thinking puzzles, games, and apps that help players work on cognitive abilities such as attention, memory, and executive functioning.

Through her writing, community involvement, workshops and public speaking engagements Ruth brings hope and education to brain injury survivors and their support and helps build that invaluable bridge between the two sides of brain injury. In addition to her first book, *Being Brain Healthy*, Ruth shares her insights and proven techniques for amplifying everyday experiences on www.craniumcrunches.com and www.insidersguidetotheinjuredbrain.com.

Dear Brain,

I am almost done grieving the losses.
The loss of my keys, the loss of my words, the loss of
where I fit in the world.
As peace sets in and I find a comfortable level to float
It really is time to honor, celebrate, and thank you for
all I found.
Within your imperfections, I learned to listen closely
And I found my voice, calling me to action.
Within the fog I walked into a deeper understanding of
what is around me
And I found the focus I needed to see the beauty right in
front of me so much more clearly.
Within the confusion, I learned to look for clues in
context
And I found the insight that comes with shifting my
perspective.
Within the fear of doing it all wrong I heard the
laughter
And I found the key to my survival.
Within the world of believing that no one could possibly
understand I discovered a community
And I found my purpose.

With deep love and gratitude,
Ruth

Made in the USA
San Bernardino, CA
24 February 2019